Maintenance Planning, Control and Documentation

Second edition

To my wife Alice
for her understanding and support
in this and many other projects

Maintenance Planning, Control and Documentation

Second edition

E. N. White

Gower

First published in Great Britain by Gower Press Limited 1973

This edition published 1979 by Gower Press, Teakfield Limited.

Reprinted 1982 by Gower Publishing Company Limited,
Croft Road, Aldershot, Hants, GU11 3HR, England

ISBN 0 566 02144 7

 British Library Cataloguing in Publication Data

White, Edwin Neville
Maintenance planning, control and documentation.
— 2nd ed.
1. Plant maintenance
I. Title
658.2'02   TS192

Printed in Great Britain by
Biddles Ltd, Guildford, Surrey

Contents

Illustrations

Preface

The engineering consultant, visiting many locations and seeing many different maintenance situations, in government, industry and commerce, can identify the types of problem which confront the manager of the maintenance function and can list those solutions which are most helpful and cost-effective. This book is an attempt to record some of this experience in ways that will be of practical help to the responsible manager. It therefore deals with maintenance management generally rather than advocating any particular approach. The importance of maintenance support systems is emphasised because so often, where management systems and planning methods are applied and subsequently fail, the cause can be traced to poor logistics.

The book is recommended to support training programmes for all levels of maintenance management and supervision, and has been tested with classes of students from many countries. Chapters 1 to 4 will also be of use when introducing the maintenance department to managers of related departments (finance, production, estates, works management, etc.).

Inflation in the 1973-79 period has not only increased maintenance and spare parts costs but has also increased plant replacement costs to levels which make maintenance aspects all-important in any assets management programme. The increasing expenditure on plant and services installations in modern buildings (hotels, hospitals, office blocks) is reflected by changes in this second edition, with emphasis on assets rather than production machines and with 'loss-of-use' costs included with 'loss-of-output' costs as the possible effects of downtime.

The opportunity has been taken to introduce 'terotechnology' which provides a broader view of the maintenance function and, in particular, relationships with other relevant departments. The terotechnology system demands an understanding of 'life cycle costing', an introduction to which has been included. The sections dealing with 'condition monitoring' and the role of computers in the maintenance department have been expanded, and the emerging usefulness of the mini-computer as a maintenance planning and information processing device made clear.

E. N. White

Acknowledgements

Grateful acknowledgement is due to the following for permission to use information and illustrations, and for examples of maintenance documents:

Reed Corrugated Cases Ltd — Examples of maintenance control documents
Kalamazoo Ltd — Sample maintenance control documents
Woodcon Products Ltd — Planning boards
Addressograph Multigraph Ltd — Job specification cards
Comprehensive Maintenance Services Ltd — Computer systems
National Terotechnology Centre — Plant information exchange
H. B. Maynard and Company Ltd — Work measurement systems
Lubecon Ltd — Lubricant handling equipment
Seaflame Company Ltd — Contract servicing documents
M and E White Consultants Ltd — Product support and maintenance manuals
J. Hodsman and Son Ltd — Engineering drawings systems
B and K Laboratories Ltd — Vibration testing equipment
SPM Instrument UK Ltd — Shock pulse equipment
Muirhead Vactric Components Ltd — Chip detectors
Duckhams Ltd — Lubricant analysis
Static Systems Group — Time-shared monitoring
Honeywell Ltd — Centralized surveillance

Publisher's Note

The illustrative material in this book is drawn from the actual documents used by companies, to whom acknowledgements are expressed on the previous page.

The need for a standard format in book production means that the size and proportions of many documents have had to be modified in the following pages. The essential information carried by each form, however, remains unaltered. Firms using this book to design or adapt their own systems and records will, of course, draw up forms of a shape and size to suit their own requirements, adding appropriate data covering company name, reference numbers or dates, specific instructions, etc.

1

Introduction

The pressures on those managers and supervisors who are responsible for the provision, operation and maintenance, and eventual disposal of physical assets (buildings, structures, plant and equipment) grow as investment costs increase, output or usage values increase, automation spreads, labour patterns change, international competition or comparisons take effect, and management for profit or for continuity of use demands a planned and controlled approach to assets management. The manager of the maintenance function – whether the job title is estates manager, works manager, chief engineer, plant engineer, buildings manager or maintenance manager – is attracting more attention than ever before in his or her long record of service to the owner/user, as the importance of cost-effective maintenance is understood. The growth and spread of inflation in the late 1970s gave rise to a new awareness of the rising values for downtime or loss-of-use, not only in productive industry but also in supermarkets, public services, hotels, transport systems and hospitals. At the same time, asset replacement costs became so inflated that increased and well-managed maintenance programmes to extend the life of existing assets were essential aspects of senior management strategies, in particular where renewal or replacement of assets at current prices could not be financed from earnings.

It has been said that the very inevitability of maintenance is the factor which tends to obscure its importance. Certainly there is a long record of neglect of the application of management techniques in many maintenance departments and an even more general record of failure to provide adequately for maintenance when plant or buildings are designed, built and sold. This book recognizes the importance of maintenance and records a number of techniques used to improve efficiency in the maintenance department; not only to control rising costs and to improve operational effectiveness but also to develop a controlled (managed) situation in this vital area of activity.

From the point of view of the investor in buildings and plant the main reasons for 'improving' maintenance methods are:

1   Protection of the investment in buildings and plant by regular and adequate maintenance to ensure high utilization and long life, at acceptable life cycle costs.
2   Safeguarding the employment of the personnel and the return on capital or the maintenance of services from the project, be it factory, hospital, administration building or other equipped building, or from the machine or equipment if it is fixed or mobile plant.
3   Providing for technical and operating independence of the 'in-plant' staff who are charged with maintenance of output or service.
4   Controlling maintenance costs and developing useful operating records to assist in future budgeting and in definition of procurement policies.
5   Establishing a safe working environment based on safe buildings and safe plant.

From the line manager's point of view the reasons for 'improving' maintenance methods include:

1   Protecting the buildings and plant
2   Increasing utilization and reducing downtime
3   Controlling and directing the labour force
4   Economizing in the maintenance department
5   Maximizing utilization of resources
6   Maintaining a safe installation
7   Recording expenditure and costing work
8   Preventing waste of tools, spares and materials
9   Improving technical communication
10   Providing cost records for future budgeting
11   Measuring plant performance as a guide to future procurement policies.

Considerable light was thrown on the maintenance situation within British industry by the government report issued in 1970 (Reference 1). This indicated that in manufacturing industry alone the national expenditure on engineering maintenance was £1,100 million per year and that staff productivity could be raised to save £200–250 million of this amount. Furthermore, inadequate maintenance affected production in some 20 per cent of plants and a further £200–300 million could be saved by improvements in indirect maintenance costs. Other comments indicated that many companies were not employing preventive maintenance techniques; many were failing to plan corrective work; there was a failure to record performance, costs and downtime, and a need for training at all levels. The total national expenditure on maintenance if buildings maintenance and maintenance in the nationalized and service industries was included was estimated to be in excess of £3,000 million per year. This report stimulated the Government-sponsored terotechnology programme (see Chapter 2) which identified the role of maintenance in assets management. Its potential can be judged if the figures quoted above are updated for inflation and other factors to present-day values.

Individual cases of maintenance improvement have shown remarkable results and substantial benefits, with staff made available for capital and other work by the reduction in standby and emergency work, with costs stabilized, productivity increased and production losses much reduced. However, even when performance is already apparently satisfactory in a given plant the introduction of planning and control methods is desirable to establish a managed situation in which any future undesirable trends can be identified and countered.

Effects of Automation

The widespread application of automation techniques and the development of sophisticated process-control systems introduces a new level of responsibility for, and increased dependence upon, the maintainer. Some of the reasons for this are:

1   Plant output capacities are raised, making downtime more costly, and loss-of-use costs are similarly increased to produce high consequential losses during failures.
2   Dependence on control systems can produce total disruption of output when one machine or other element in a process fails.
3   The possibilities for operator intervention to compensate for machine errors or failures are decreased.

The effects upon the maintenance department have included:

1   A requirement for new skills (e.g. in repair of computer-controlled systems).
2   A need for improved multidiscipline working (e.g. on mixed electronic/hydraulic/pneumatic systems).
3   A requirement for a systems approach to maintenance, especially fault-finding and repair.

In many situations the introduction of automation has changed the production worker/maintenance worker ratio, mainly by a reduction in the number of operatives employed. Where increases in maintenance complements are resisted, improved management techniques, planning, training and technical information systems (as outlined in this book) are necessary to enable the maintenance staff to meet the new demands upon them. The figures for maintenance costs and ratios given in this chapter will vary according to the extent of automation introduced into a particular plant. The effects of automation will require careful study by the maintenance manager and will be set out in the objectives and strategies section of his budget (see Chapter 11). Careful attention to procurement (Chapter 10) is necessary if appropriate counter-measures are to be introduced.

Definition of Terms

(The various forms of maintenance and the relationship between them are shown in Figure 1:1.)

Terotechnology: a combination of management, financial, engineering and other practices applied to physical assets in pursuit of economic life cycle costs.
  NOTE: Its practice is concerned with the specification and design for reliability and maintainability of plant, machinery, equipment, buildings and structures; with their installation, commissioning, maintenance, modification and replacement, and with feedback of information on design, performance and costs.
Breakdown maintenance: work implemented after failure but based on advance planning.
Condition-based maintenance: corrective maintenance resulting from condition monitoring.
Corrective maintenance: work intended to restore an asset to the acceptable standard.
Emergency maintenance: work caused by unforeseen breakdown or damage.
Life Cycle Costs: the total cost of an item throughout its life including initial costs, costs of ownership and costs of downtime.
Maintenance: work undertaken to keep or restore an asset to an acceptable standard at an acceptable cost.
Planned maintenance: work organised and carried out with forethought, control and records.
Preventive maintenance: work intended to preserve an asset, to prevent failure and to detect incipient faults.
Running maintenance: work implemented with the asset remaining in use.
Shutdown maintenance: work only implemented when the asset is out of service.

Availability: period for which asset is in a usable state.
Check: to examine and compare with standard.
Condition monitoring: frequent or continuous checks made to determine the 'health' of an asset and to expose incipient faults.
Downtime: period for which asset is not available for use.
Assets register: an inventory of assets.
Maintenance management: the organization of maintenance within an agreed policy.
Maintenance schedule: a comprehensive list of maintenance and its incidence.
Maintenance planning: establishing in advance the work to be done and the

methods, tools, labour resources and timing necessary.

Overhaul: a comprehensive examination and restoration of an asset or part of an asset, to an acceptable standard.

Test: to compare with an acceptable standard.

User: anyone for whom the asset performs a service.

Vendor: person or company selling buildings, plant or equipment.

For a comprehensive definition of terms used in maintenance organization the reader is referred to British Standard 3811: 1974, *Maintenance Terms in Terotechnology.*

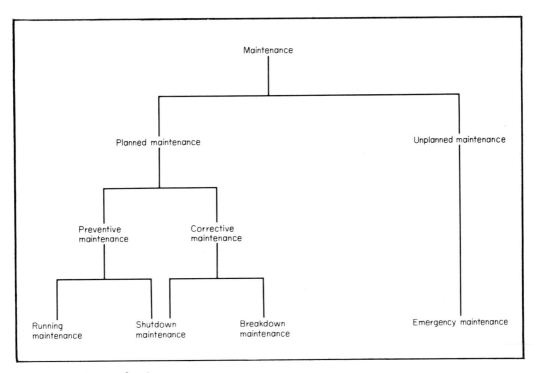

Figure 1:1 Types of maintenance

Appendix: Maintenance costs

The costs of maintenance in various companies within an industrial category vary widely according to the accounting practices, management methods and cost allocations systems adopted. Thus, the following figures give only general guidance to trends within particular groups.

1 *Food, Drink and Tobacco*	%
Maintenance staff as percentage of total direct labour	12
Maintenance labour allocations	
Plant maintenance	57
Buildings	7
Capital projects	13
Services	16
Maintenance cost allocations	
Internal maintenance department	98.8
External labour and subcontract	1.2
Maintenance by production staff	0
Cost allocations in internal department	
Labour	42.8
Materials	29.7
Overheads	27.5
Allocations of maintenance expenditure	
Planned work	41
Breakdown work	30
Minor repairs, etc.	29
Maintenance costs as percentage of sales	1.94

2 *Paper, Printing and Publishing*	
Maintenance staff as percentage of total direct labour	9
Maintenance labour allocations	
Plant maintenance	62
Buildings	12
Capital projects	7
Services	17
Maintenance cost allocations	
Internal maintenance department	92.3
External labour and subcontract	7.4
Maintenance by production staff	0.3
Cost allocations in internal department	
Labour	51.2
Materials	24.4
Overheads	24.4
Allocations of maintenance expenditure	
Planned work	49
Breakdown work	11
Minor repairs, etc.	40
Maintenance costs as percentage of sales	3.87

3	*Textile Industry*	%
	Maintenance staff as percentage of total direct labour	10
	Maintenance labour allocations	
	Plant maintenance	68
	Buildings	17
	Capital projects	5
	Services	9
	Maintenance cost allocations	
	Internal maintenance department	99.6
	External labour and subcontract	0
	Maintenance by production staff	0.4
	Cost allocations in internal department	
	Labour	40
	Materials	35.5
	Overheads	24.5
	Allocations of maintenance expenditure	
	Planned work	26
	Breakdown work	34
	Minor repairs, etc.	40
	Maintenance costs as percentage of sales	3.16
4	*General Engineering*	
	Maintenance staff as percentage of total direct labour	11
	Maintenance labour allocations	
	Plant maintenance	52
	Buildings	19
	Capital projects	13
	Services	12
	Maintenance cost allocations	
	Internal maintenance department	89
	External labour and subcontract	10.8
	Maintenance by production staff	0.15
	Cost allocations in internal department	
	Labour	39
	Materials	21
	Overheads	40
	Allocations of maintenance expenditure	
	Planned work	16
	Breakdown work	46
	Minor repairs, etc.	38
	Maintenance costs as percentage of sales	3.44
5	*Electrical Engineering*	
	Maintenance staff as percentage of total direct labour	10
	Maintenance labour allocations	
	Plant maintenance	73
	Buildings	11
	Capital projects	5
	Services	6

Maintenance cost allocations	%
Internal maintenance department	90
External labour and subcontract	9.8
Maintenance by production staff	0.2
Cost allocations in internal department	
Labour	31
Materials	20
Overheads	49
Allocations of maintenance expenditure	
Planned work	29
Breakdown work	39
Minor repairs, etc.	32
Maintenance costs as percentage of sales	2.36

6   *Clothing and Footwear*

Maintenance staff as percentage of total direct labour	4
Maintenance labour allocations	
Plant maintenance	68
Buildings	15
Capital projects	6
Services	10
Maintenance cost allocations	
Internal maintenance department	100
External labour and subcontract	0
Maintenance by production staff	0
Cost allocations in internal department	
Labour	34
Materials	36
Overheads	30
Allocations of maintenance expenditure	
Planned work	23
Breakdown work	35
Minor repairs, etc.	42
Maintenance costs as percentage of sales	2.44

2

Terotechnology

Definition

The terotechnology concept grew from the study of maintenance practices (Reference 1) mentioned in Chapter 1. Its scope is illustrated by the definition:

'A combination of management, financial, engineering and other practices applied to physical assets in pursuit of economic life cycle costs.'

This indicates quite clearly the thinking behind the concept, namely that attention to maintenance management alone would not provide the complete answer to the problems arising in the maintenance sector (or otherwise attributed to maintenance). It clearly was necessary to look at other management functions having an influence on the performance and costs of physical assets: in other words, those functions which contribute to assets management. Some of these are illustrated by Figure 2:1.

The broad application of the terotechnology concept is further illustrated by the note to the definition, which states:

'Its practice is concerned with the specification and design for reliability and maintainability of plant, machinery, equipment, buildings and structures; with their installation, commissioning, maintenance, modification and replacement, and with feedback of information on design, performance and costs.'

Thus the terotechnology concept is applied to both buildings and plant, and to all stages of their life cycles from design to eventual replacement or disposal. Finally, the terotechnology system includes the feedback of data to produce management information.

The terotechnology system (Figure 2:1) is generally shown as a combination of management systems and communication channels which provide support for maintenance. Typical contributions include:

Design — assets designed for maintainability and reliability.
Procurement — application of 'best buy' procurement techniques (Chapter 10).
Projects — provision of assets having operability and maintainability features.
Operations — introduction of operating techniques which reduce downtime and improve care of assets.
Finance — cost control, cost monitoring and feedback (Chapter 11).
Personnel — selection and training programmes for operating and maintenance personnel.

Strategies for Terotechnology (New Assets)

Terotechnology is concerned with the provisioning and subsequent management of physical assets. Assets management is a cradle-to-grave strategy which commences with techno-economic studies prior to an investment and proceeds through the implementation cycle into the life cycle of use. During the period of use there will be operation and maintenance strategies, designed to give best use at least cost and eventually a replacement or disposal strategy will be formulated, based on technical and economic reviews.

Asset provisioning can be considered in three phases; the preparation phase, decision phase and implementation phase. In the preparation phase it is important to consider historical data and feedback from operations and maintenance, and to attempt whole life predictions with life cycle costs. These and other data are considered during evaluation and decision, and it is important here to consider the views of operations and maintenance management. Finally, in the implementation phase the programme includes design, installation, commissioning and proving stages until the assets are handed over to the operations and maintenance personnel. Some important considerations in these phases are listed in Figure 2:2.

The utilization phase requires the planned operation and planned maintenance of the asset with performance analyses and feedback of management information to influence present and future policy. Feedback of performance should be recorded and used to benefit future designs and further procurement decisions, and for review during frequent examinations of the whole life predictions. It is important also to apply controls to any modification programmes so that configuration control is maintained. Finally there will be a review phase when all technical and economic factors are considered and the decision made to dispose of, or replace, the asset. Additional feedback from these reviews can be used to benefit design, procurement and future developments. The terotechnology system demands that a number of 'trade-off' decisions be made. For example, the comparison between increased utilization from a new asset and the attendant costs of operation and maintenance, especially if new technologies are incorporated, can be considered in a 'trade-off' against statistics for the assets to be replaced.

Strategies for Terotechnology (Existing Assets)

Actions to implement terotechnology principles in the management of existing assets may be considered in two groups — actions within the maintenance function, and actions by other departments. Each of these groups further divides into — actions which follow accepted practice, and actions based on analyses of feedback.

As an example, within the maintenance function, the application of planning and control to maintenance work is probably the first reaction of many managers to a terotechnology programme. The principles are well-documented, case histories exist and planned maintenance is accepted practice. However, at a later date, when the feedback inherent in a planned system is analysed, the control system may well be modified and condition-based maintenance introduced. It is the actions based upon feedback which effect the most significant improvements but it is often necessary to improve existing systems as a first step, so that meaningful analyses can be made as justification for further progress.

Guidelines for maintenance actions in a terotechnology programme are given in this book as follows:

Action	Chapter	Benefits
Introduce maintenance planning	3	Protection of capital assets Control of maintenance costs and resources Contributions to health, safety and energy savings.
Analysis of feedback	4	Control of costs and resources Quantitative data to support further plans.
Develop hierarchy	5	Improved communication and relationships Stated responsibilities and strategies.
Increase training programmes	6	Development of management and worker skills Introduction of new techniques.
Introduce work planning	7	Improved management of resources Improved productivity. Reduced downtime.
Improve stock control	8	Support for work programmes Improve materials management.

Action	*Chapter*	*Benefits*
Improve maintenance information systems	8	Support for training and upgrading programmes Support for fast fault diagnosis and repair.
Introduce condition monitoring	9	Control of preventive maintenance costs Prevention of loss and damage.
Improve procurement practices	10	Introduction of 'best buy' selection Reduction of life cycle costs Improved maintenance support systems.
Introduce costing systems	11	Improved costs management and feedback.
Prepare budget objectives	11	Development of strategies for maintenance improvements, and identification of cost benefits.

A number of important actions which contribute to a terotechnology programme are identified in Chapter 7 under the heading 'Maintenance Improvement'.

Applications of terotechnology practices by other managers can include:—

Management Function	*Action*
Estates Management	Introduce life cycle costing Employ investment appraisal techniques Improve procurement methods, see Chap.10 Develop communication and feedback systems Plan and control buildings maintenance.
Plant Ownership or Management	Introduce life cycle costing Talk terotechnology to suppliers Plan and control maintenance Introduce feedback and records systems Consider uses for condition monitoring Review maintenance support systems.
Manufacturing Management (plant or equipment)	Base marketing strategy on life cycle costs Base designs on reliability and maintainability Talk terotechnology to customers Review quality control and quality assurance

Management Function	*Action*
	Review customer service and support systems, especially spare parts service and technical manuals.
Management Accountants	Introduce life cycle costing and current cost accounting methods Develop meaningful systems to assist analyses of feedback Encourage expression of strategies and trade-off evaluations in departmental budgets.
Purchasing Managers	Talk terotechnology to suppliers Insist on user/maintainer participation in purchasing decisions Include life cycle costs, reliability and maintainability aspects in all specifications Specify support items accurately (see Chap.10).
Designers	Consider life cycle costs and performance Introduce design recording, design review and design disclosure systems Review reliability and maintainability aspects with user/maintainer Ensure commissioning specification proves the design intent Provide for maintenance policies, particularly condition monitoring.
Production Manager or User of Assets	Consider operational aspects of life cycle costs Provide for operations/maintenance liaison Train operatives in assets care Allocate time for essential maintenance — both preventive and corrective.
Maintenance Manager	Plan and control maintenance activities Develop communication and feedback systems Analyse costs, performance and technical factors Introduce condition-based maintenance Provide adequate maintenance support

Management Function	*Action*
	(information, spare parts and training)
	Participate in procurement decisions with particular attention to maintainability, reliability and life cycle costs.
Technical Sales Managers and Staff	Talk terotechnology with the customers
	Feed back customer comments to the planners or designers
	Talk reliability, maintainability and life cycle costs with the designers
	Check support requirements and the proposed support provisions for compatibility
	Examine all health and safety aspects of the product in each application.

Training in Terotechnology

It has been said that there will never be a terotechnologist as such, although some logistics engineers and some maintenance consultants have developed combined approaches to many aspects of applied terotechnology. Many managers, including those in the list above, can benefit from a general introduction to the terotechnology system, with guidance for its application to their specific responsibilities. An outline of some training programmes which follow this principle appears in Chapter 6. Many terotechnology practices present the commonsense and obvious approach to assets management, with the terotechnology system providing a check list of desirable actions and acting as a trigger to their application at the correct time and in the right sequence.

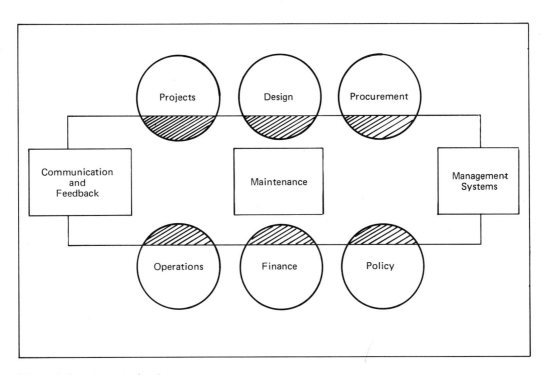

Figure 2:1   A terotechnology system

PREPARATION PHASE
    Consideration of Feedback (Operations and Maintenance)
    Planning (Operating and Maintenance Policies)
    Technical Forecasting
    Whole Life Planning
    Life Cycle Costing

DECISION PHASE
    Direct participation by Users (Past and Future)
    Preparation of Procurement Check Lists, see Appendix 1
    Reviews of Supplier Profiles and Quality Ratings
    Specification of Support Systems, see Chapter 8
    Review of Life Plans and Life Cycle Costs

IMPLEMENTATION PHASE
    Design (Design Records, Design Reviews, Configuration Control)
    Studies (Maintainability, Reliability, Feedback from Users)
    Project Planning and Control
    Support Planning (Information, Training, Spare Parts)
    Information Systems (Disclosure of Design Data by Manufacturers and Suppliers)
    Preparation of Documentation (Manuals, Specifications, Training Programmes)
    Maintenance Planning (Management Systems and Resources)
    Commissioning (Testing, Defect Action, Certification)
    Handover (Operation, Proving, Final Acceptance)

UTILIZATION PHASE
    Operation, Maintenance, Condition Monitoring
    Technical and Costs Records
    Analysis of Records
    Feedback to Operations, Maintenance, Design, Procurement
    Improvements and Updating (Configuration Control)
    Reviews of Life Plans and Life Cycle Costing

REVIEW PHASE
    Technical and Financial Reviews
    Disposal or Replacement Decisions
    Feedback to Benefit Future Projects

Figure 2:2   Terotechnology considerations in a life cycle

3

Maintenance
Planning and Control

Total maintenance planning embraces all activities necessary to plan, control and record all work done in connection with keeping an installation to the acceptable standard. This includes preventive maintenance and corrective maintenance, planned overhaul, planned replacement, spares provisioning, workshop functions, repairs and renewals, plant history compilation, plant modification to facilitate maintenance, spare-parts manufacture, preventive maintenance on spare-parts, etc. In a fully controlled situation only the time spent on emergency work is 'unplanned' and this could well be less than 10 per cent of the available man-hours in the maintenance department. The three basic requirements of a planned maintenance system are:—

1   A programme of maintenance activity for the buildings, plant and equipment.
2   A means of ensuring that the programme is fulfilled.
3   A method of recording and assessing results.

Figure 3:1 lists the basic elements of a planned maintenance system which is represented diagrammatically in Figure 3:2.

Assets Register

A comprehensive register of all plant and buildings (or of that part of the plant and buildings which are the subject of the planning) is an essential base for the planning operation. Each asset must be positively identified in terms of:—

1   Name and code.
2   Description.

3   Reference numbers — manufacturers, suppliers (if any), users.
4   Location — with provision for changes if item is interchangeable or mobile.
5   Supplier's details.

The asset code can be numerical, or alpha-numerical and replaces any existing building or plant numbering systems. Asset codes are given to buildings, plant, services installations, and mobile plant and are attached to the asset for identification purposes. The codes can be used in a variety of ways (see Figure 3:3) and are preceded by other codes when used for corporate purposes (investment analyses, depreciation calculations, etc.). Asset codes can identify asset type (PU = pump), accounts codes (primary and secondary) and physical locations. Additional numbers can be added to link the basic asset codes to spare parts, special tools, work specifications, or to drawings and manuals filed in the maintenance library. It is helpful if the accounts codes and location codes coincide. The asset code must be used on all work cards, defect reports, materials requisitions and other documentation as the key to effective communication and feedback.

Other optional information may include:

1   Financial data — initial cost, depreciation, etc.
2   Ancillary equipment — pumps, motors, etc.
3   Special requirements for services — air, water, etc.
4   Details of items suitable for substitution.

In general, asset registers are compiled in card-index form (see Figure 3:4), or in a plant register book. Frequently an index system is used for basic data in one of the fast-access forms available; the expanded information being contained in a register or card file.

When the items are recorded, their classification into divisions and subdivisions is very important. Any medium- to large-sized register can be subdivided in terms of: —

1   Asset usage/availability;
2   Technical groups; or
3   Maintenance methods.

For example, classification by usage is convenient when plant is maintained section by section — either because the plant is available one section at a time or because the usage of the various sections varies. In a pharmaceutical factory the usage of plant in the ingredient-storage section is quite different from that in the high-speed packaging department. Classification on technical groups allows for the different engineering disciplines used — electronic instrumentation and hydraulic winches, for example, obviously have very different maintenance requirements. Classification by maintenance method is important as some items may be the subject of contract maintenance, some maintained only by planned overhaul, others on an exchange basis. Items subject to special statutory requirements (boilers, lifting gear, nuclear installations, etc.) are also separated. Frequently the subdivisions of a register will be arranged (with some duplication if essential) so that requirements in more than one classification can be met.

Further subdivisions of the register will depend upon the recommendations of the planning engineer or consultant and may include:—

1   Division of major assets into sub-assets.
2   Listing of motors and drives (particularly if these are interchangeable items).
3   Separation of items subject to statutory inspections.

The type of information recorded will vary with the uses to which the data are to be put. The simplest case merely provides for maintenance control. In other situations a complete financial record is kept so that extra costs, depreciation, modification changes, and so on, may be added or subtracted to provide a continuous record of the standing value of the item and ultimately the life cycle costs.

The assets register is the information centre of the planned maintenance system. In a small engineering works with 50 or so machine tools it may be contained in a box-file. For a large process plant, a nationalized undertaking, or for a group of hospitals, the register may be maintained by a computer. A wide choice of systems exists between these extremes.

Maintenance Schedules

Maintenance schedules list the requirements of each asset shown on the register in so far as routine maintenance is concerned. A typical schedule card (see Figure 3:5) indicates:—

1   Grade of labour required.
2   Frequency of the work to be done.
3   Details of the work to be done.
4   Estimated time for the execution of the work.

Where assets are identical or similar the schedules are repeated on additional cards so that a card exists for each asset and a complete requirement for every item is recorded. The preparation of the maintenance schedule is a skilled task because not only must all necessary maintenance activities be identified and recorded, but the frequencies must be evaluated with availability for maintenance in mind as well as other more obvious factors including vendor suggestions.

Grouping of the work by slight adjustments of the frequencies can have a most beneficial effect on the operation of a maintenance programme.

Basic data can frequently be obtained from manufacturers' manuals but not all manuals have the necessary information, or have the information in the required form. The maintenance planning engineer must therefore use any available information as a basis but must interpret it in accordance with the local requirements and with his own knowledge and experience. (Obviously care must be taken within the guarantee period of new equipment to conform with any special instructions which form part of the vendor's guarantee.)

Other decisions to be taken by the maintenance planner will include:

1   Which of the preventive maintenance tasks can be carried out with the machine running and which will require a shutdown period? How long a shutdown is required?
2   What spares will be required for a particular situation so that these can be made available?
3   What are the lubrication requirements? These are often specified on a separate schedule so that lubrication routines with operator routing programmes can be established, for use by the lubrication operatives.

Work Specifications

Precise specifications for the activities on the schedule vary in depth and presentation according to the system, the local labour requirements, the complexity of the items to be maintained, etc. In the simplest case the maintenance schedule tells the engineer what to do and how often it should be done and the detailed technical information is obtained directly from manufacturers' manuals. Reference to these is made on the work cards issued to the maintenance staff.

A simple maintenance work card with references to manufacturers' manuals is suitable for plants employing relatively high-grade labour where detailed work specifications are considered unnecessary.

A detailed work specification is shown in Chapter 8 and this indicates the type of specification prepared when full technical control is required or when work study and productivity agreements are to be introduced as a means of improving efficiency and productivity in the maintenance department. The introduction of positive work-control systems, from simple manpower resourcing through to work study and productivity deals requires a degree of timing and the work specification is essential for this purpose.

Whether or not work measurement is to be applied the maintenance planning engineer must provide estimated times for each activity as a basis for manpower resourcing.

Work specifications are presented either as part of the work card or as a separate document. The master copies may be retained in the control office and photocopies issued for use in the factory. Specifications may be separate documents (sometimes with technical illustrations) and can be issued as cards or as manuals. If produced as cards and plastic covered to prevent wear they can be issued from the control office or the maintenance store and returned after use for reissue with the next 'trigger'.

Much of the maintenance work can be specified in detail — preventive, overhaul or corrective. Specifications for corrective work are subject to modification in content and frequency as experience is gained. When convenient, corrective work may be timed to coincide with an overhaul task or with production stoppages.

Maintenance Controls (Triggers)

When the extent of the preventive maintenance activity is known a suitable control system can be selected to 'trigger' the correct activities at the required frequencies. Control systems range from a manually sorted card file, through a range of automatic job-card sorter/printer devices to a computer-controlled system in which a computer print-out represents the complete programme for the selected period.

If maintenance in a number of locations (for example, various buildings within a local authority district or a number of factories within a group of companies) is to be controlled from a single source, the expenditure on both hardware and software can be minimized by use of one central control system. As a general guide, the capacities of the various methods are:

> 0– 5,000 activities — card index
> 1,000–20,000 activities — sorter/printer (manual)
> 5,000–80,000 activities — sorter/printer (automatic)
> 3,000 upwards — computer system

The term 'activity' refers to the items on the schedule, not those on the register. Thus an asset having 4 sections maintained on 4 different frequencies generates 16 activities.

If a computer-based system is used a study will be necessary, as with the introduction of any data-processing system, to determine the availability and the cost of programs, the cost of installation, and the availability of computer time on any existing installation. When installing a computer-controlled system based on time from an existing computer it is necessary to safeguard the availability of that time before abandoning existing methods and accepting full computer dependence (see Chapter 4).

The functioning of a typical control system is illustrated by Figure 3:6. When introducing the plan, the immediate task is to make an inventory and prepare the assets register followed by the maintenance schedule. The 'trigger' system gives rise to the issue of the work card and the issue of materials; the detailed instructions (work specification) are issued at the same time. At the completion of the scheduled work the documents are returned to the control office for recording and for any corrective work to be initiated.

Manpower Resourcing Schedule

Having determined the routine maintenance requirements of the items on the assets register it will be necessary to prepare summary sheets giving hourly totals from the various grades of labour employed.   A typical summary timesheet is shown in Figure 3:7. The times for the maintenance activities in the various time periods are recorded and are summed in trade groups. Annual totals are then prepared both in terms of grades of activity and also in terms of grades of labour. Allowances are then added for activities which have time periods extending beyond one year (for examples two years, three years, four years, etc.) and maximum cumulative hours in a five-year period may be established if required. In most systems this type of time-sheet is only required to provide total hours over a one-year period.

Manpower resourcing in the maintenance department only makes sense when full control and full support for the maintenance activity is provided. The routing of maintenance staff during work is important because the time taken to reach the work situation has an important bearing on the total man-hours employed. Studies have shown that 15 per cent of the available working time can be devoted to obtaining instructions and making journeys to the work point in an industrial installation of average size. The route followed by staff engaged on routine maintenance activities must be considered by the planning engineer during the planning phase. Full support in terms of test equipment, spare parts and technical manuals can reduce the number of journeys made to workshops or the stores.

Maintenance Records

The operation of an effective maintenance records system provides the following information:—

1 The percentage of planned work achieved in the period.
2 The ratio of planned to unplanned work.
3 Downtime for the period.
4 Ratio of preventive work to corrective work.
5 Maintenance requirement comparisons between individual assets, between types of asset, or between groups of assets.
6 Indicators for reliability of the products of particular manufacturers.
7 Trends in spare-parts consumption.
8 Equipment failure patterns.
9 Performance details for personnel, by individual or by trade group.
10 Materials used, for guidance on restocking policies.
11 Indicators on possible standardization policies.

Records are kept in many different ways, ranging from card files to computer stores. The labour required for updating records of work done is a deterrent to many managers and can only be justified if use is made of the information. If a computer is used, lengthy print-out sheets can be time-consuming also. However the computer is a useful tool for providing summary information on a regular basis so that trends can be observed. Whatever system of records is used detailed investigations have to be reserved for individual situations in which the cost is justified.

In a simple system a practical level of recording is obtained by writing on the actual work card as issued. Successive workers on the plant can refer to the working history and to their predecessors' comments. This can be useful in passing on the defect history or wear trends but can precondition the worker in his approach to the work, sometimes to bad effect. Other simple systems provide for the issue of new cards but for up to six or ten of the completed cards to be retained in the control office at any time to give a short history record (see Figure 3:8). Thus with a two-monthly activity the continued retention of six cards would produce a one-year history. These systems do not provide detailed financial records which would be provided on separate cards or as a function of the company accounts department.

Liaison with the User

Effective liaison between the operating managers or planners and the maintenance planners is essential to the operation of the maintenance programme. The depth of the liaison depends upon the method of operation, the worst situation occurring when continuous use is required. However, in continuous-process plants the awareness of the requirement for liaison is generally such as to encourage efficient planning. The most difficult situations occur where the degree of use or the volume of production fluctuates and a peak period can coincide with an intended maintenance activity.

In an ideal working environment both long-term (annual) and short-term (monthly) plans are regularly reviewed. Short-term release of assets for maintenance purposes can substantially reduce the need for weekend working by maintenance staff. Among the disadvantages of weekend working are the supervision problems, nonavailability of materials, spares, and other services at weekends, and possible personnel problems as the maintenance staff tend to become socially separated.

Another aspect of liaison is the request for service originated by the operatives. When standby maintenance staff are available, requests for assistance are frequently made verbally. Formal requests include details of the fault and of the particular item requiring attention together with a priority indication, advice as to whether operations have been halted and an indication of the trade group (see Figure 3:9).

Cost code information is required for any work undertaken by the maintenance staff in response to requests by operatives. Depending upon the cost codes breakdown this permits expenditure to be allocated to particular machines, to individual buildings or to particular operator stations.

Planned Lubrication

The service provided by lubricant vendors is used by most maintenance managers when setting up a planned lubrication system. This is particularly useful where individual machines may have 30 to 40 lubrication points requiring six different oils or greases. It is also useful in plants where, although the number of application points may be less, careful planning of the route followed by the oiler or greaser is essential not only to reduce the time taken but also to ensure full attention to every application point. The problems of planning are less acute in domestic types of installation (office blocks, etc.) and the application of lubricants is usually made a part of other preventive-maintenance schedules. However, it may still be useful to rationalize the oils and greases used.

The oil company's planning engineers begin by making an inventory of the plant to be included in the survey, unless this can be extracted from an existing assets register. The schedule is then extended by the addition of lubrication information including:

1   Number of application points.
2   Frequency of each application.
3   Method used (grease gun, oil can, etc.).
4   Amount required.
5   Type of lubricant required.

From this register the planning engineer develops a rational approach to the lubrication requirements of the plant including:

1   Total work-load assessment having regard to the number of points and the frequency of application.
2   Subdivision of the work load to indicate manpower requirements.
3   Development of effective routes between the application points.
4   Provision for plant shutdown when necessary for lubrication.
5   Provision for access (ladders, etc.) and for extended oil pipes or grease lines to reduce access times.
6   Development of identification techniques − labels on the machines or pictorial work-specification sheets.
7   Rationalization of lubricants whenever possible.

In preparing this plan the engineer takes due account of environmental and operating conditions and the recommendations of plant vendors. When new equipment is included any provisions of the guarantee which affect lubrication have to be provided for. A lubrication schedule is shown in Figure 3:10.

Planned Overhaul

In some high-utilization plants (such as those of food and packaging manufacturers) it is still accepted policy to limit overhaul work to that which can be included when a product change is made or an actual breakdown occurs or when an annual shutdown is scheduled during the operators' vacation period. This requires a high degree of planning if all necessary parts and materials are to be made available at the right time. This type of overhaul work can suffer in quality through undue haste at the time and can prove expensive if unforeseen problems arise in the work period. It does have applications, particularly in processes where rollers, dies, and other major tool items have to be replaced during a product change.

It is more general, however, for overhaul periods to be scheduled as part of the total maintenance plan. The frequency of overhaul may be based on vendor recommendations, on estimated life periods for active components, or on monitoring of the machine by vibration analysis, etc. (see Chapter 9). In the long-term the plant history cards are of some assistance in establishing frequencies. Wherever possible the introduction of a planned maintenance system should include not only preventive maintenance of the routine kind but also planned overhaul based on built-in monitoring techniques. Thus it may be necessary to budget for monitoring facilities when considering plant procurements.

Another aspect of overhaul shutdown planning is found in those installations in which an annual closure occurs in the vacation period. In many situations it is unwise or uneconomical to operate at reduced throughput levels and a planned closure of perhaps two weeks is preferred. Planning for this period takes place long before the closure. Planned overhaul schedules are used to establish a work programme and to execute resourcing in men and in materials. At national holiday periods the situation is often complicated by the closure at the same time of other service companies leading to difficulties in obtaining lubricants, welding gases, spare parts, tools and transport, etc. It is therefore essential that a thorough planning exercise be carried out and all information provided (Figure 3:11). Work will then be supervised by a nucleus of permanent staff retained during the holiday period and supplemented by contract labour from external sources. In this respect the plan must indicate the numbers and grades of labour required over the period. In some large installations the planning and organization of an overhaul period is a full-time occupation for a planning engineer who is located in a planning office fitted with multi-layer planning boards or a computer. As the cost of downtime rises with intensive use, high-volume production and inflationary trends the timing of the restart after such a closure is of prime importance. It is essential, therefore, that the programme is maintained according to schedule.

Of vital importance to the planning of overhaul work is the question of plant standardization during procurement. The project planner must consider this aspect most carefully and ensure that whenever possible compressors, pumps, motors, air-conditioning plant, machine tools, and even items of process plant are standardized as far as possible. If this is not possible on major plant items, then ancillary items on the major plant can sometimes be standardized (drive motors, for example). This not only permits the interchange of items at time of breakdown but also encourages the provision of strategic spares so that exchanges can be made and items can be overhauled in local or central workshops without delay to the user or without waiting until the overhaul period arises.

An exchange-for-overhaul system may be operated through central workshops if a number of installations in one area are standardized as far as possible during procurement. The importance of this aspect cannot be overemphasized and the direct involvement of engineering and maintenance specialists at the procurement stage is essential to provide for this.

Quality Control

It is possible to apply the concepts of quality control to maintenance work, as follows:

1   Dismantle item in accordance with work specification or vendor's instructions.
2   Remove as many parts as possible which are subject to wear and replace with spare parts from stores.
3   Reassemble and test item in accordance with specification.
4   Return to service.
5   Apply quality control test to all worn parts, returning to stock only those which meet the required standard.

In this way the asset is tested in accordance with the specification, the remaining parts are tested in accordance with recommended tolerances and specifications, and a degree of quality control is applied which ensures that the asset and those items of spares selected for reuse are in accordance with specification.

Manpower Allocation

In the operation of a planned maintenance system staff of appropriate skills have to be allocated to various tasks in accordance with the requirements originated by the control office. The actual method of allocation may be a simple manual system or a computer program but this is one aspect of planning in which good-quality supervision on a local basis often produces the best results.

A basic programme of planned work must originate from the control system with a batch of work cards issued for the particular period. However, the issue of these cards to particular personnel is still, even in quite sophisticated systems, a matter for personal control by the foreman/supervisor. There are many local factors which may affect the decision on sending Mr Smith or Mr Anderson on particular routes on a particular day. The system is satisfied if two men in a given labour grade are matched to a two man-day load but a correct selection by the foreman can maximize efficiency.

In some installations the work allocations are made by the foreman by the simple practice of placing the work cards (and work specifications if used) in wall-mounted racks provided with the names of the incoming labour force (see Figure 3:12). In other installations the work cards issued to the foreman may be allocated on a more formal basis with local manpower allocation records maintained by the foreman and returned to the control system to provide indications of work done, work not completed, etc.

Downtime Analysis

The maintenance records must provide for an acceptable level of downtime analysis, either from the records themselves or in direct summary form from the maintenance requests. Useful information produced in this way includes:

1 An indication of downtime per building, per machine, or if necessary per operator.
2 The time taken for fault diagnosis and repair on various types of fault, or on specific machines, or by various personnel.
3 Indications of the causes of breakdown.

Among the useful points made clear by analysis (1) might be:

(*a*) The true ratio of downtime to use time (to answer rumours or inaccuracies being quoted against the maintenance department).
(*b*) The need for further investigation, by the maintenance management, of high downtime areas.
(*c*) The relationships between operator performance and downtime on individual assets.

Analysis (2) may help to define:

(*a*) High downtime areas where permanent standby repair staff or zone workshops might be beneficial.
(*b*) Suppliers to be avoided on future procurements.
(*c*) A requirement for specific training (e.g. electronic fault-finding) for maintenance workers.
(*d*) The most efficient members of the maintenance staff for the various types of work (fault-diagnosis, repairs, renewals, etc.).

Analysis (3) will define:

(*a*) The spare parts and materials requirements for the various assets.
(*b*) Any requirement for increased operator training.

(*c*) Problems caused by variations in the product materials used in manufacturing processes.

An example of a typical report appears in Figure 3:13.

It will be seen that the information provided by a downtime analysis is complementary to any cost-analysis work. However, downtime recording in detail is relatively expensive and, if economies are sought, may be applied only in certain areas rather than generally. The areas chosen may be high-risk areas containing plant which is vital to a high production figure, or may be areas of rising maintenance cost as defined by the normal cost summary, or areas in which large consequential losses could occur.

Asset Reviews (Audits)

Plant or buildings may be subjected to technical or financial reviews (sometimes referred to as audits). The financial review on any particular machine or building is facilitated if the register cards are of the type containing full cost data for the initial purchase and subsequent expenditure (see Figure 3:14). Alternatively this data may be provided by the works cost accountants from the financial control department.

The true initial cost of the machine contains the installation charge, commissioning cost, standby costs for the proving period, the cost of spares, ancillary equipment, test gear and services.

The running costs include depreciation, interest on capital, replacement costs for spares, modifications, additional tools, access equipment, test gear and other ancillaries, also any vendor servicing or staff-training costs. Only when all the relevant costs are taken into account can the true initial cost and the true annual running cost be quantified.

Some plant is replaced by new as a result of accurate financial reviews which indicate rising operating costs. However, many more replacements are the result of technological change, changes in product requirements or demands for increased output or manpower reductions. Possibly an increased use of the financial review would stimulate effective comparisons of maintenance costs between existing and possible replacement machines, although in some cases such a review has resulted in retention of existing plant with acceptably low maintenance costs in normal usage.

Technical reviews fall into two classes: the review of present capability against that of a modernized installation and the regular audit of a machine or building to check performance. As stated earlier much of the plant replaced is in fact made redundant by advances in technology, not only machine technology but also product technology. Also in this category are replacements made to economize on labour, space or services. Regular performance audits, however, are made to ensure that the machine or plant is performing satisfactorily and remains in the optimum condition for consistent output with minimum maintenance. Examples of this need for audits are seen in continuous process plants where calibration and repair is in the hands of a variety of workers spread over a number of shifts. In such an environment a machine may be operated in a number of states according to the particular ideals or misconceptions of the various shift personnel. A technical audit restores the optimum state.

Costing

The maintenance control system must provide for accurate costing of work and materials for all maintenance activities. Work cards, materials requisitions, work instructions, maintenance requests, defect reports and time sheets must all carry significant codes to indicate cost allocations. The level of accounting practice adopted will determine the structure of the code system which may define costs in terms of:

1   Individual factories.
2   Process lines.
3   Individual machines.
4   Separate buildings.
5   Office units.
6   Administration departments.
7   Canteens and other special areas.

There are a wide variety of functional and physical hierarchies which may be adopted. Costing procedures are described in detail in Chapter 11. The cost codes can conveniently be incorporated in the asset numbers (see Figure 3:3).

Shutdowns

In many situations a six-monthly, annual or five-yearly closure is planned during which essential maintenance or plant replacement is carried out. An annual shutdown often coincides with the fixed holiday period of the staff. This shutdown work requires careful advance planning if maximum productivity is to be achieved and this includes:

1   Activity selection and planning.
2   Labour resourcing including use of contractor's men.
3   Planning of spare parts and materials supplies.
4   Materials, tools and access equipment provisioning.

The activity planning for annual shutdown in a large plant can be the function of a permanent planning staff. Some of the planning charts described in Chapter 7 can be used and planning display boards as described in Chapter 4 help to present the intended programme. The use of computer programs to process shutdown data and to predict critical paths and the various requirements of the plan is now accepted (see Chapter 4).

Labour resourcing is an important aspect of planning and must be based on estimated job times supported by accurate benchmark times for known tasks such as stripping and reassembling pumps, etc. in the workshops. The supplier of contract labour can be called upon to augment the internal staff when the requirements are known. This also reinforces the need for adequate advance planning.

Materials, tools, handling equipment and spare parts require scheduling especially in view of the possibility that some suppliers may be closed for vacations at the same period. When checking spare parts it is not wise to rely upon the label on the package, but to thoroughly check the suitability of the spare inside the package for the task in hand. Some advance work may be necessary in the preparation of the spares for use – cleaning, minor adjustments, etc.

It is also important to check the maintenance library and to ensure that the relevant drawings and technical manuals are available before work is commenced.

The planning office will also indicate the possibility of carrying out certain work in advance of the shutdown, also the possibilities for establishing test rigs for checking work after completion and in advance of the restart. A pump testing rig, for example, can avoid the need for running-in pumps or dealing with a failure caused by incorrect assembly when the plant is returned to service. Downtime at the time of restarting is as costly as downtime at any other period but is frequently a much more serious blow to the prestige of the maintenance manager and his staff.

Health and Safety Aspects

The operation of maintenance planning contributes significantly to industrial safety because:

1   A well-maintained safe plant remains in a safe state.
2   If priorities are maintained the most important work is done first and not neglected.
3   Statutory requirements will be met.
4   Safety interlocks, guards, overloads, safety valves, etc. will be regularly checked.
5   The possibility of pollution is reduced, where these risks exist.

Within the maintenance department itself there is a safety problem if maintenance of the department's own equipment is not scheduled. Portable tools, extension leads, ladders and other access equipment require regular care in the interest of safe working. Close and continued cooperation between the safety officer and the maintenance manager is essential.

A safety audit will provide a general indication of safety standards and should be repeated at regular intervals. The inspector may be a safety officer or a supervisor from the works department. The results will show if any corrective action is necessary, or if a more intensive study of any aspect should be made. The audit will indicate:

1 If the Health and Safety at Work responsibilities are fully understood by departmental staff.
2 If adequate explanatory literature is distributed.
3 If fire precautions and equipment are adequate.
4 If the asbestos regulations are understood and complied with.
5 If the abrasive wheel regulations are complied with.
6 If a planned maintenance system is operated to keep assets in a safe condition.
7 If the plant and machinery has adequate guards and safety circuits.
8 If the system for statutory inspection of boilers, pressure vessels, lifts, etc. is satisfactory.
9 If the safety regulations for high voltage electrical equipment are complied with.
10 If the general attention to safety can be improved by training programmes, information, notices, signs, safety equipment or revised operating and maintenance procedures.

Maintenance Support Organization

All maintenance depends upon effective support in terms of materials, spare parts, technical manuals, lifting, handling and access equipment, also special tools, jigs and test gear. In a large maintenance department a separate section of personnel with a supervisor may be employed to manage the support activities. In a smaller department it is frequently more difficult to ensure that all ancillary equipment is safeguarded yet at the same time remains readily available. A support item sometimes overlooked is the planned maintenance of the tools, equipment and spare parts themselves; in particular spare parts which are located in the working area ready for use, and may have been contaminated.

Examples of tool records are shown in Figures 3:15 and 3:16.

Buildings Maintenance

Expenditure on buildings and properties may conveniently be expressed as 'revenue costs' (those costs incurred on normal repairs and maintenance) and 'capital costs' (the cost of new work, adaption and repair above the level of work necessary to maintain the property in good working condition). Basic cost groups include building maintenance, site maintenance and external services.

It is usual for the buildings maintenance force to be an integral part of the works department, responsible through the chief engineer or maintenance manager to the management. The staff employed on structural or site maintenance constitute a separate section if the installation is a medium-to-large one but in medium-to-small size installations also undertake labouring and other appropriate duties on general maintenance. The maintenance of fixtures and fittings, also services (water systems, electric lighting, etc.) is also scheduled by the buildings maintenance section if the size of the installation permits the employment of specialist tradesmen allocated to this work.

Classifications of work undertaken by the buildings maintenance section include:

1   External decoration.
2   Internal decoration.
3   Main structure (including windows and gutters).
4   Internal construction (including partitions and doors).
5   Fittings (shelves, closets, etc.).
6   Plumbing and sanitary services.
7   Mechanical, gas and air conditioning services.
8   Electrical services (including kitchens).
9   External and civil engineering works.
10 Routine cleaning.

These may constitute the main divisions of the 'buildings' section of the assets register and the divisions of the cost code system. Further subdivisions are made as required and in accordance with the size of the installation. All routine maintenance work and planned overhaul work can be scheduled in the same manner as is plant maintenance.

The available technical information on buildings and their fixtures usually consists of plans and specifications with some technical brochures in support of the fittings, air conditioner units, etc. However, buildings maintenance manuals are now more common and some excellent examples can be seen on some Government building programmes.

Item number	Item name	Description
1	Assets register	A complete inventory of the buildings and plant to be maintained.
2	Maintenance schedule	Schedules for inspection, lubrication and preventive maintenance of the items in the register. The schedules may also include planned overhaul.
3	Work specifications	Instruction cards or documents which identify exactly the tasks to be undertaken within the maintenance system.
4	Maintenance control system	A 'trigger' system which initiates the activities on the maintenance programme at pre-determined intervals as listed on the maintenance schedule.
5	Resourcing schedule	A manpower allocation system to ensure that the resources are available to implement the maintenance requirements of the assets and that optimum use is made of labour.
6	Maintenance records	A record of maintenance carried out and a system for reporting to management.
7	Maintenance support organization	The organization of technical information, spare parts and tools, etc.
8	Liaison with production	An effective system of agreeing with the user management when maintenance work can be done.
9	Planned overhaul	Provisions for ensuring the planned overhaul of plant, either on a regular basis in accordance with the maintenance schedule or in response to condition monitoring.
10	Costing system	Costing procedures to ensure adequate cost control and apportionment of costs in the maintenance department.
11	Training	The necessary training of operatives and supervisors in the operation of the system.

Figure 3:1   Components of a planned maintenance system

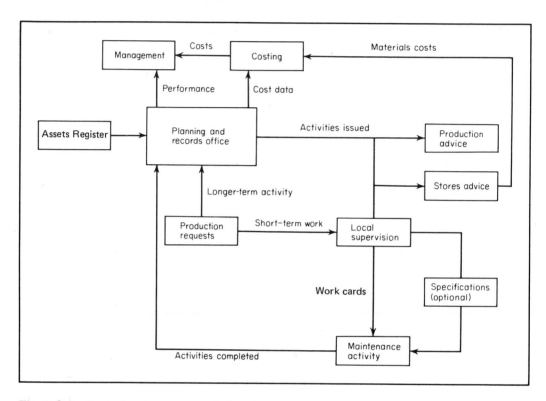

Figure 3:2 Typical maintenance control system

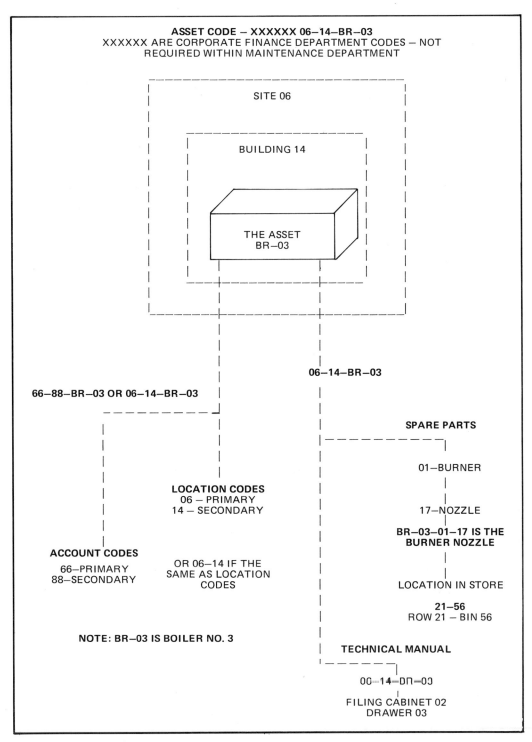

Figure 3:3   Assets coding

Asset Card No. 1 0

Company

Asset No.

Location

Name		Area

Manufacturer

Manf. Address

Supplier

Suppliers Address

Telephone Number

Telephone Number

Order No. — Invoice No — Acceptance Date — Warranty

Ref. numbers — Model No.

Description

Sub. Asset			
001		002	
003		004	
005		006	
007		008	
009		010	
011		012	

MOTORS	Function	Manufacturer	Ref. Number	Location	Hp/kw	Rpm	Volts	Ph	Type	Rating	Size	Card No.
1												
2												
3												
4												
5												
6												
7												

Date Completed:— Completed by:—

Financial Record — See over—

man-cam

TOTAL MAINTENANCE SYSTEMS

© Comprehensive Maintenance Services Ltd. P.O. Box 257 West Byfleet KT14 6AZ Printed in England 1978

Figure 3:4   Asset register card

Planned maintenance card		Number		
		Section		
Location	Team	Standard time each		
Item number	Plant description	Inspection period	CCN	Standard time

Figure 3:5   Planned maintenance card

The maintenance schedule is recorded on the front and a record of work done on the reverse side. This type of card may be issued directly to staff or a photocopy made

Record of maintenance completed											
Date	Name	Clock number	On	Off	Supervisor's signature	Date	Name	Clock number	On	Off	Supervisor's signature

Item number	Parts renewed	Date	Initials	Item number	Parts renewed	Date	Initials

Item number	Date	Plant needing further attention

Figure 3:5 — continued

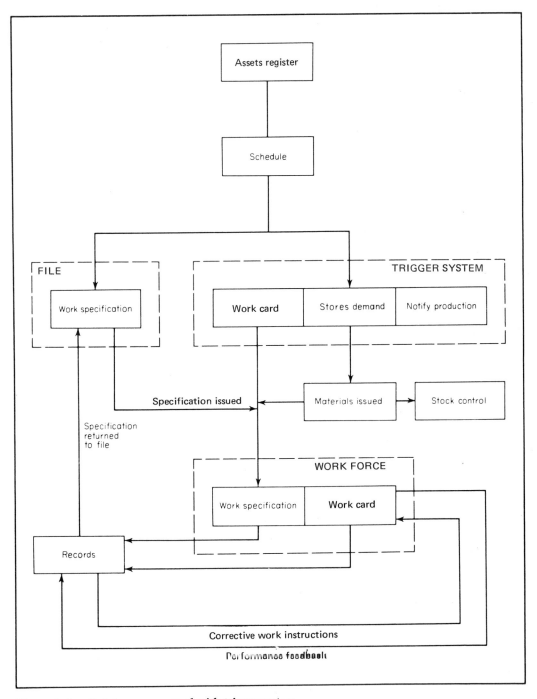

Figure 3:6   Maintenance control with trigger system

CODE			1W	2W	4W	13W	6M	1Y	2Y	3Y	4Y	5Y	LUB.	ELEC.	MECH.	INST.
TOTAL HRS.																
ANNUAL																
COMMITTED HOURS PER YEAR								TRADE HRS. PER YR.								
ALLOWANCE FOR ADDITIONAL YRS.																
ALLOWANCE FOR ADDITIONAL YRS.																
ALLOWANCE FOR ADDITIONAL YRS.																
ALLOWANCE FOR ADDITIONAL YRS.																
MAXIMUM CUMULATIVE HOURS IN 5 YR. RANGE																

Figure 3:7   Manpower summary sheet

Plant history card		

Description _____   Cost centre number _____

_____   Plant number _____

Location _____

Planned maintenance card numbers _____   Lubrication record card numbers _____

_____   _____

_____   _____

_____   _____

_____   _____

General information

Date	Details of work carried out	Job card numbers

Figure 3:8   Plant history card
The numbers of work cards relating to the plant item are recorded together with work details

Service request				Serial				
From	Department	Machine number		Supervisor's signature				
To	Department	Factory number		Date				

Please attend to the following work:

In emergency, ring 525

Date	CL number	Factory	C C N	Service request number	On	Off	Hours	Standard time

Brief description of work carried out

To be completed by engineering section

Urgent				
Within 24 hours	Maintenance			
To suit work loading	Planned maintenance			
Weekend	Works order	Works engineer's signature	Date completed	Supervisor's signature

Figure 3:9 Service request card

Issued by the production supervisor, this card has space for indication of urgency

Lubrication Card No. 5 0

Company

Name

Asset No.

Location

Area

Ref.	Lub. point description	Lub. point Location	Apps	Frq	Lub	Meth'd	Oper	Catg.	time	Related Activity		

Date Completed:— Completed by:—

© Comprehensive Maintenance Services Ltd. P.O. Box 257 West Byfleet KT14 6AZ Printed in England 1978

man-com
TOTAL MAINTENANCE SYSTEMS

Figure 3:10 Lubrication schedule

drive shaft oil seal (U) in plate, ensuring that knife edge of oil seal (U) faces inside of mechanism.

22. Refit bearing seal plate (F) with new joint, and tighten six bolts evenly.

    Note
    Grease oil seal surface before fitting over drive shaft (S).

23. Turn mechanism right side up and check drive (S) and driven shaft (H) for end float as follows:-

    (1) Push drive shaft (S) as far as possible in one direction and check distance from end of shaft to seal plate (F) using a straight edge against end of shaft.

    (2) Push drive shaft (S) as far as possible in the opposite direction and check distance.

    (3) Measure end float between end of driven shaft (H) and edge of mechan-ism housing, with shaft in extreme positions. The difference in measure-ment is the total end float and should be 1/16 in. ± 1/32 in. If readings are above or below the limits, either thinner or thicker gaskets should be inserted between housing and seal plate and bearing caps as necessary.

24. Refit bearing caps into correct positions with new joints and tighten bolts evenly.

Figure 3:11   Part of overhaul procedure document
This must be accompanied by suitable engineering drawings, preferably exploded perspective drawings

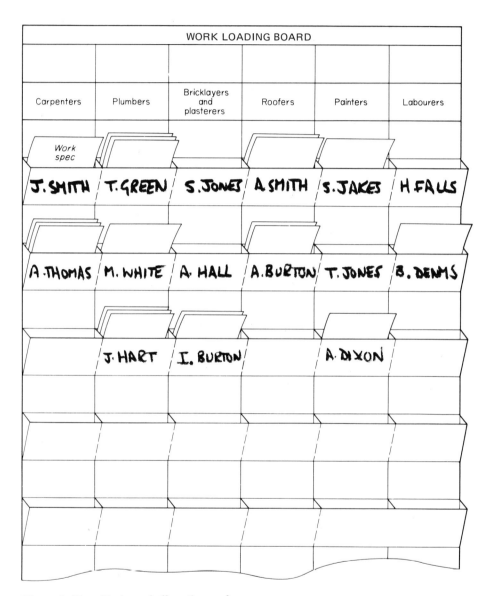

Figure 3:12   Work-card allocation rack

Date	Item	Fault	Downtime (hours)
1	Main panel	Fuse blown	0.1
2	Spreaders	Latches snapped, main arm	1.3
6	Mixers	Gearbox shaft broken (spare gearbox fitted)	0.25
10	Main press	Burst pipe (guard to be fitted)	0.3
11	Water sprays	Valve burnt out (revert to manual — no spare)	0.1
15	Water sprays	New valve fitted	0.4
16	Dryer burner	Faulty electrode (spare fitted, jets cleared)	1.20
19	Compressor	Bearing collapsed (spare fitted — re-order)	3.00
22	Product lift	No upward drive (contacts cleaned)	0.4
24	Main press	Burst pipe (repaired — guard fitted)	0.5

Figure 3:13   Record of downtime — New Mill Plant

Figure 3:14 Plant and machinery record (financial)
This form provides a complete financial record of the item including depreciations, additions and eventual disposal (Kalamazoo)

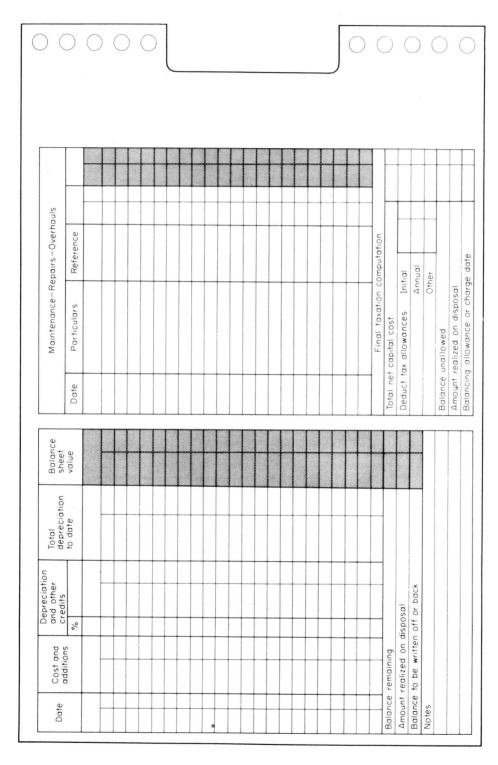

Figure 3:14 — continued

REPAIR / REPLACEMENT NOTE

DATE _____

TOOL NO. / SIZE   PART NO.

TOOL DESCRIPTION

REMARKS _____

_____

_____

COLOUR	WHITE	PINK	BLUE
CODE	REPAIR STATION	TOOL PROGRESS	INSPECTION RECORD

Figure 3:15   Tool repair/replacement note
The note is completed in triplicate and the copies distributed as noted (Kalamazoo)

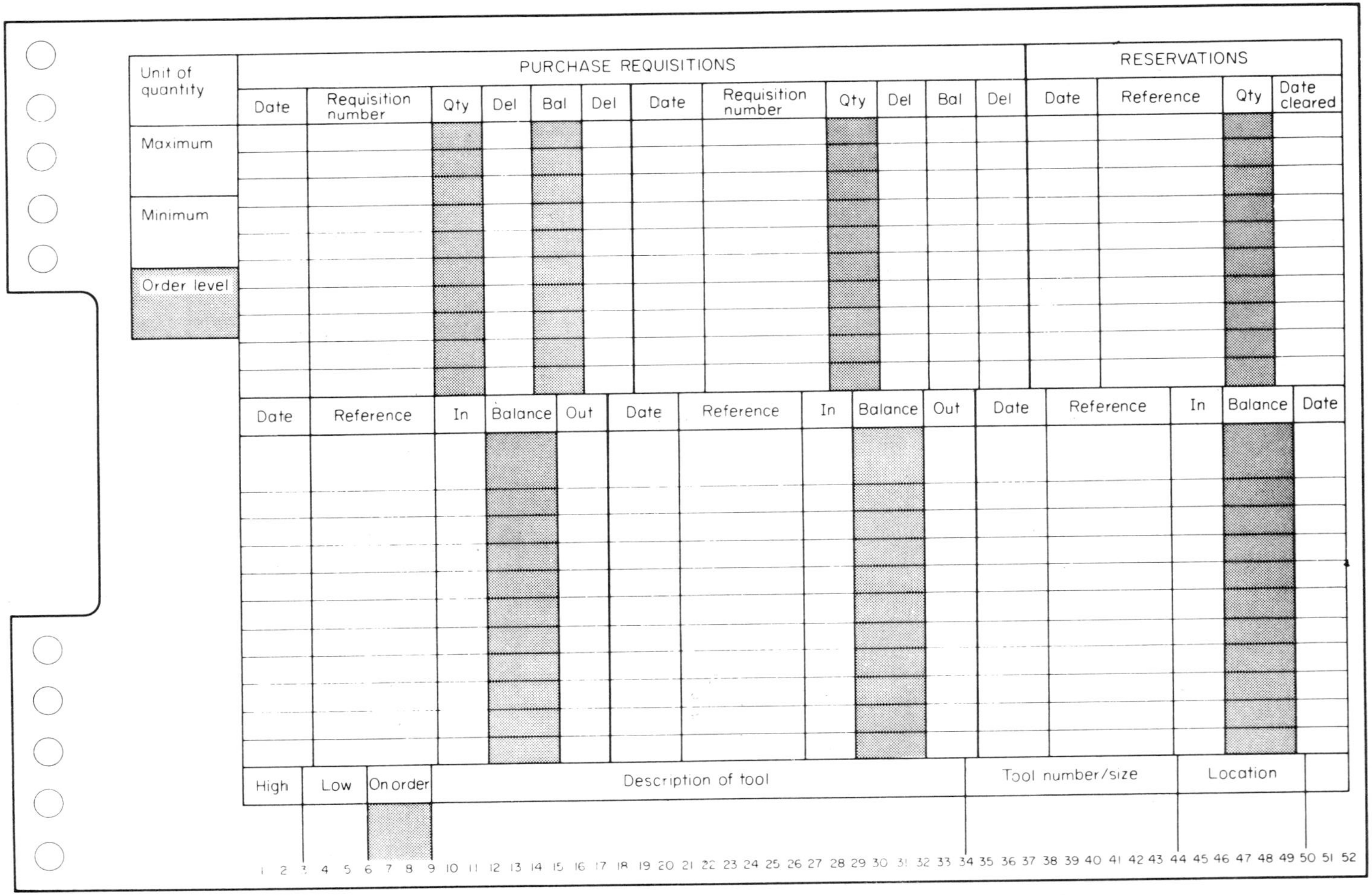

Figure 3:16 **Tool-store stock record form** (Kalamazoo)

Date	Reference	In	Balance	Out	Date	Reference	In	Balance	Out	Date	Reference	In	Balance	Out

Figure 3:16 – continued

BOILER MAINTENANCE RECORD CARD

NAME & ADDRESS		DATE OF AGREEMENT	
		CONTRACT PRICE	
		PLANNED PAYMENTS	YES/NO
		INSURANCE POLICY NO.	
		BOILER MAKE & BURNER TYPE	
A/C. OF		BOILER CAPACITY	Btu/h
			k/W
		WATER PUMP MAKE	
		WATER PUMP ELIGIBLE FOR REPLACING	YES/NO
A/C. NO.		PLANNING CARD REF.	

| TELEPHONE NO. | GRADE OF OIL |
| INSTALLER | SPECIAL INSTRUCTIONS |

DATE OF INSTALLATION

DATE	TYPE OF CALL	INVOICE/ WORK NOTC. NUMBER	ENGINEER	TIME SPENT	REMARKS AND/ OR PARTS FITTED

Figure 3:17 Boiler maintenance record card (Kalamazoo)

4

Typical Control Systems

Card-Index

Even in the smallest works department a group of assets may be maintained in a planned and controlled way by use of a small card-index. Each card refers to a particular maintenance activity (weekly, monthly or annual) using a particular trade skill (electrician, greaser, etc.) on an individual asset. Each card is complete in that a monthly activity card also contains the weekly activity or daily activity coincident with it. Thus each card contains a complete record of work to be done by a given trade skill at a particular time.

The file is divided into 52 weekly sections, each week containing a proportion of monthly and weekly activities to provide a balanced work load for the various trades employed. At week 1 the cards are removed from section 1 for action and the activities of annual frequency are issued for action. (These include the appropriate weekly, monthly and quarterly tasks within those activities.) The weekly, monthly and other cards are returned to the file, the weekly cards to section 2, the monthly cards to section 5, etc. This ensures their reissue at the correct frequency. The annual cards are returned to section 52 of the file, or to section 48 if a 48-week cycle of activities is preferred. Daily routines are listed separately.

This very simple system can be operated by a supervisor and is easily updated or modified as necessary. A signature and technical comments may be entered on the card by the maintenance man, or a photocopy issued for workshop use and the original retained in file. The copy is filed or the details entered on the master cards to provide a record of work done and technical trends.

Card-index systems of maintenance control may be operated from edge-punched or other coded cards (Figure 4:1). Card selection machines are available which electrically or mechanically select the required cards from a file. In the 'Factfinder' system the edges of the cards are hand-punched to provide a retrieval code. Programme bars are inserted in the magazine of a small electrical vibrator which shakes a group of cards until those required become offset and may be extracted. The punch marks may be positioned to indicate the grade of labour, type of plant, frequency of activity or other information. A wide range of standard cards, also facilities for special requirements, are available. The system can be operated on a part-time basis by a clerk, the cards for 3,000 machines being sorted into trade groups and frequencies in 45 minutes. The cards are not issued to the maintenance personnel but are photocopied so that the original remains clean. The copies are signed on completion to provide a maintenance record.

Card-index systems also provide a convenient method of recording plant registers and maintenance histories (both technical and financial) (Figures 4:2 and 4:3). When compiling a plant record a register book is maintained in which each line is given a sequential number. The book may be prepared using a hand-operated sequence numbering stamp. When machinery is received, or is recorded from existing plant, the name is written opposite the next number in sequence. A metal tag is issued with the number stamped on it together with an 'asset information' form. A fitter is detailed to attach the tag to the machine and to return the form with details obtained from the manufacturer's nameplate, etc. The number from the register, together with the details from the machine information form, provide the basis for completion of the master record card. Further information may be requested from the vendor or from the maintenance office as necessary, also from the procurement office correspondence regarding the plant.

If required, additional card files may be used to provide cross-references to the register in alphabetical order, or in location order. The location details are an essential part of recording and must be updated if the item is relocated. Various types of record cards are obtainable, designed to accommodate financial information, technical information, or both. Special designs are produced to meet individual requirements. Record cards may be filed in loose-leaf binders or in metal filing trays.

Special categories of plant which merit special card-indexes in separate file binders or filing trays include steam-raising plant, pressure vessels, lifting gear or other plant subject to statutory inspections. Tools are also recorded separately, all items over a certain value being capitalized. This applies not only to portable tools, access equipment, lifting gear, etc. used in maintenance work but also to dies, cutters, rollers and other specialized production tools. A tool record system provides the following advantages:

1   The history of the tool is available.
2   Tools under repair or replacement are recorded.
3   Tools are readily recovered for reissue and use.
4   Pilfering and damage are reduced.

The maintenance diary and copy-strip system (Figures 4:4 and 4:5) provides a low-cost yet flexible method of producing maintenance work lists that permits a detailed appraisal of the programmes at a glance. Each activity is typed on a card strip which is mounted on a plastic copy-strip holder in a plastic binder. Strips can be removed or added without disturbing the sequence of the records.

Long-term maintenance tasks (quarterly, annual, etc.) are recorded in the long-term binder or binders. These are split into 52 sections (one for each week of the year). Card strips are typed for each activity (one for the annual, four for quarterly, etc.) and are loaded into the binder to provide the required balance of work load throughout the year. Then at the end of each week the copy-strip pages for the following week are removed and photocopied to produce work programmes for the supervisors. As many copies as are required for the supervisors and the maintenance men are produced. These copies are issued to the men by the supervisors with the items for which they are responsible marked. After use, the sheets are signed by the men and returned by the foreman to the control office.

When work is held over because of priorities or nonavailability of men, machines or materials, the activities concerned may be given a priority rating and incorporated in the next programme. In this case, additional strips are prepared and added to future programmes as required. These must be removed and destroyed after copying. If the activities are to be recorded as 'not done' and left until the next time they become due for service then a note is made on the work programme. The clerk then applies red adhesive symbols to the next identical strips for those activities. When this is next photocopied the symbol appears on the work programme, indicating the need for priority attention. Alternatively, work not done can be indicated on the diary by yellow adhesive symbols which do not reproduce when the copies are made. This provides an indication throughout the diary of the percentage of planned work not achieved during the year.

Short-term tasks, weekly and monthly, can be recorded in another diary which is divided into five sections as follows:

1   Weekly activities.
2   Monthly activities, week 1.
3   Monthly activities, week 2.
4   Monthly activities, week 3.
5   Monthly activities, week 4.

The monthly activities are split over the four weeks and each week the appropriate section is printed for distribution, together with the weekly tasks. Similar arrangements may be made for dealing with daily or fortnightly activities, dividing the register as necessary. Yellow adhesive symbols can be used to provide the basis of an annual summary of the percentage of planned work not achieved. Standard times can be inserted on the strips if these times are determined. These may be made known to the men if required or may be obscured by a masking strip when the photocopies are made. In one of the examples shown a transparent overlay is included, the effect being that after photocopying the instructions appear as an engineering maintenance programme sheet with spaces for remarks and time summaries.

The advantages of the system include:

1   The diary presents a clear, ready-reference picture of maintenance work programmes.
2   Work held over can be identified and reprogrammed.
3   Work sheets are photocopied and do not require additional typing or writing effort.
4   Frequencies may be changed, items added and items deleted simply and quickly.
5   Examination of performance and comparison of time taken with standard times is provided for.

Lubrication schedules may be issued separately or may be included within the instruction 'Check main drive unit' as issued in the work list. If issued separately a separate diary is compiled and schedules issued as illustrated in Figure 4:5. The operation of a scheduled lubrication programme by separate personnel (greasers and oilers) may be timed to occur with the check by the fitter or electrician, particularly if plant is shut down for access. If operating separately the greaser or oiler must report any noticeable defects or any undesirable features which could lead to failure.

A detailed specification of the work necessary to 'Check main drive unit', for example, may be issued. This can be a separate sheet of paper, issued with the work list from the control office or issued by the local supervisor on receipt of the work list. If the work specification is produced on a standard work card it may be issued to the men via a loading board as described later.

Loading Boards

Loading boards, affixed to the wall in the planning office or the maintenance workshop, provide a convenient method of issue for work cards, work specifications, work lists, etc. They may also be used for machine loadings in the maintenance workshop, for material control or for overhaul programming. Some of the typical uses are illustrated in Figure 4:6.

Work allocation or maintenance activity loading is accomplished in a number of ways as listed below. The appropriate method may be selected or advice sought from a consultant in the maintenance field.

Method 1

1   Work lists received from control office.
2   Work cards issued for every activity by supervisor.

3 Work cards placed in loading board against names of men allocated to preventive maintenance.
4 Completed work cards checked by supervisor.
5 Notes made of corrective work required, work cards issued and placed in loading board.
6 Work list signed and summary of man-hours completed.
7 Work list and work cards to control office.

Method 2

As above but the work cards for preventive work are mixed with the work cards for other work to provide a balanced work load, or to ensure that men working in particular locations are notified of all work at that location to reduce travelling times.

Method 3

As above but with corrective work summaries made in the control office and reissued as programmed work from that office.

Method 4

1 Work lists (3 or more copies of each received from control office).
2 Items on work lists allocated to men by supervisor adding man's name or number to selected items.
3 Work sheets placed in loading board against appropriate names. A work card may also be issued if required.
4 Signed work sheets returned to local supervisor for checking.
5 Completed work sheets returned to control office.

Work instructions may be issued as sheets or cards, preferably plastic coated or covered, to prevent wear. These may be placed in the loading board, issued from the stores, or held in suitable containers near the plant to be maintained.

Sorter/Printer Systems

The sorting and printing of work cards from a complete file of maintenance activities can be arranged by filing the basic information in the form of embossed plates. The production of cards for particular assets, individual trades or selected frequencies is accomplished automatically by use of a machine which identifies code marks on the plates, and prints only for the required activities, bypassing the remainder. The plates are held in trays which feed directly into the machine. The trays may be arranged to contain plates for any particular plant or trade or frequency if desired but such is the speed of the machine that subdivision of the file is not essential (Figures 4:7, 4:8, 4:9 and 4:10).

In the example illustrated, maintenance activities are listed on job specification cards. These are in two main sections, firstly the 'header' which indicates the machine to be worked on and secondly, the work instruction which can occupy one, two or three plates. Two cards are detached from the first section and are used to notify the planning office and the planning foreman that the job specification card is issued. The cards are coloured to indicate the trade group required; for example, yellow for mechanical and green for electrical. Figure 4:9 illustrates a card with feedback entered on the reverse side after routine maintenance has been completed. In Figure 4:10 a similar card is used for emergency work and is hand-written in the maintenance planning office. Emergency work is identified by use of a coloured card (e.g. blue) for this type of activity by any trade group.

A recent development in this field is the introduction of electronic data reading machines for analysis purposes. The work card is printed with bar codes which can be converted to punched computer tape electronically. The basic information (plant item codes, etc.) is printed by the sorting machine and additional bars are hand-written by the maintenance supervisors to indicate time taken, grade of labour, etc. On completion of the work, the work card is passed through a small electronic reading machine which produces the punched tape for analysis by computer.

Planning Boards

Apart from the loading boards referred to earlier, a wide variety of planning boards are available for work loading and programming (Figure 4:11). Among the various devices used are cards in slots, plastic symbols in slots or holes, adhesive plastic symbols and magnetic indicators. Planning boards are particularly useful for scheduling overhaul work and in some large installations the planning offices are fitted with multi-layer sliding boards which permit all-year planning of routine and overhaul work. Extensive planning is essential for annual shutdown programmes and, in the largest plants, this alone can be a full-time occupation for a planning engineer. If necessary, photographs or copies of planning boards made with adhesive symbols on plastic film can be issued to transmit the plan to a local control office or a plant location.

A Computer-Controlled System

A variety of computer systems have been developed for the management of maintenance and have provided facilities for the assets registers, work control, manpower resourcing, stock control, maintenance accounts and, in some systems, analyses of feedback and costs. In general these are based on large mainframe computers which, in industrial and commercial applications, are also employed for a variety of other purposes. This can give rise to delays, with the works department low in the order of priority for computer time, especially when major financial programmes are being run. The ideal computer system is one which is interactive, dynamic and dedicated. 'Interactive' means that it can be interrogated at short notice. 'Dynamic' means that it gives a fast response to data recording or input changes. 'Dedicated' indicates that it is always available to the maintenance department for logging vital information or for instant retrieval of data for planning or management information. These requirements can be met when using a mini-computer system within the maintenance department.

A mini-computer system (see Figure 4:12) consists of a central processor (the computer), data storage discs, visual display units and printers. The computer and its associated electronic circuits are small and can be housed in the pedestal of a typist's desk. It operates from a normal power socket and requires no special environment. The data storage discs have capacity for millions of characters of information which can be displayed on a number of visual display units (VDU). A line printer is used to provide statistical reports but, in an interactive system, is only used for exception reporting as all normal information is communicated through the VDU displays. Work cards and other single-sheet copies of the screen display are produced by a copier. In a typical installation the computer and one or two visual display units are located in the maintenance planning office. Additional units can be provided for the manager, the supervisors, the foreman, the storekeeper and in the workshops. Figures 4:13 and 4:14 show how working documents are generated for the various types of maintenance.

When introducing a computerized maintenance planning system or when converting an existing planning system to computer operation it is necessary to ensure that the data is presented in a form acceptable to the computer. This is a feature of the MANCOM system in which a manually operated master file is established and tested prior to computer operation. The file is composed of standard cards of five types, arranged in sets — one set per asset. The cards are:

Card Name	Information
Asset Record	Asset Data and Costs Record
Inventory Lubrication	Lubrication Schedule
Inventory Maintenance	Maintenance Schedule
Spare Parts Inventory	Spare Parts List
History	Feedback Record

A number of coloured inventory maintenance cards are normally used — one colour for each trade group employed. Planning charts or planning boards are used to trigger maintenance activities in the manual application.

When changing to computer control, the contents of the master file are transferred to the computer file and duplicated for security. The visual display units in the maintenance planning office are used to display work programmes which can be modified and rearranged at the touch of a button on the keyboard. The work planning and control functions include:

1   Recording or updating asset records or asset movements.
2   Managing lubrication activities and modifying the schedules if required by feedback.
3   Acting upon inspection reports from lubrication operatives.
4   Managing preventive and corrective maintenance activities and incorporating emergency maintenance when necessary.
5   Acting upon feedback from maintenance activities.
6   Resourcing for capital works programmes.
7   Acting upon feedback from emergency maintenance.
8   Managing spare parts stocks.

The storage and data handling capacity of a computer system provides the means for processing large amounts of feedback in a very short time and for presenting a variety of management information as follows:

Asset Management	– Costs, Renewal Values, Life Cycle Data, Management Ratios.
Lubrication	– Costs, Performance, Achievements.
Maintenance	– Costs, Performance, Achievements.
Spare Parts	– Stock Levels, Consumption, Trends, Costs, Strategies.
History	– Work Loads, Backlogs, Defects, Best Buys, Downtime Records, Maintenance Ratios, Condition Reports, Capital Works Progress.

Work instructions from the computer or feedback to the computer can be in full narrative or in simple codes. Some maintenance staff resist the use of codes but, with adequate consultation, codes can be introduced with benefits. Typical codes include:

Frequency codes	– W (weekly), M (monthly).
Maintenance action codes	– CHK (check), ADJ (adjust).
Condition codes	– GCD (general condition), TSN (tension).
Item codes	– GB (gearbox), SR (sensor).
Lubrication codes	– GGN (grease gun nipple).

Feedback can be in full narrative or in code or from a check list. Ticks from the check list become asterisks on the visual display unit and can be used to indicate spare parts used, spares not required, spares not available, work completed, no time available, no access and other information. Trends and unusual features can be observed immediately from the visual summary of the feedback over a period.

Other uses for the computer in the maintenance department can include:

1   Management of the works department stores.
2   Planning and control of capital works programmes.
3   Management of production tools, dies, moulds, etc.
4   Energy conservation through monitoring and control.
5   Security and fire monitoring through remote sensors.
6   Monitoring of automated processes or boiler plant.
7   Coordination of condition monitoring inputs.

The computer is a valuable tool when commissioning new assets and can provide:

1   Asset register and configuration control.
2   Register of technical manuals and drawings.
3   Register of defects and defect actions.
4   Register of tests and quality documentation.
5   Works department stores lists and spare parts quantities.

As in the maintenance planning application it is the interactive and dedicated system which provides the response and continuity needed to accommodate the many variables and the changing time scales in a commissioning programme.

Feedback Analysis

Additional value can be obtained from feedback if the analyses are made on a wider sample than that available in most individual companies or organizations. This facility is available through the Plant Information Exchange operated by the National Terotechnology Centre. Subscribers' feedback data is recorded on a computerized data base and is used to provide a variety of general costs, trends and 'best buy' information, in addition to individual feedback summaries. The source of the input data is confidential and the reports and summaries are available only to member organizations (Figure 4:15). The benefits to be expected from this type of service are:

1   Controls for ownership costs.
2   Optimized investment in maintenance stocks.
3   Management information (technical and costs).
4   'Best buys' guidance for procurement.
5   Feedback from grouped experience.

Figure 4:16 illustrates a typical record card for feedback data.

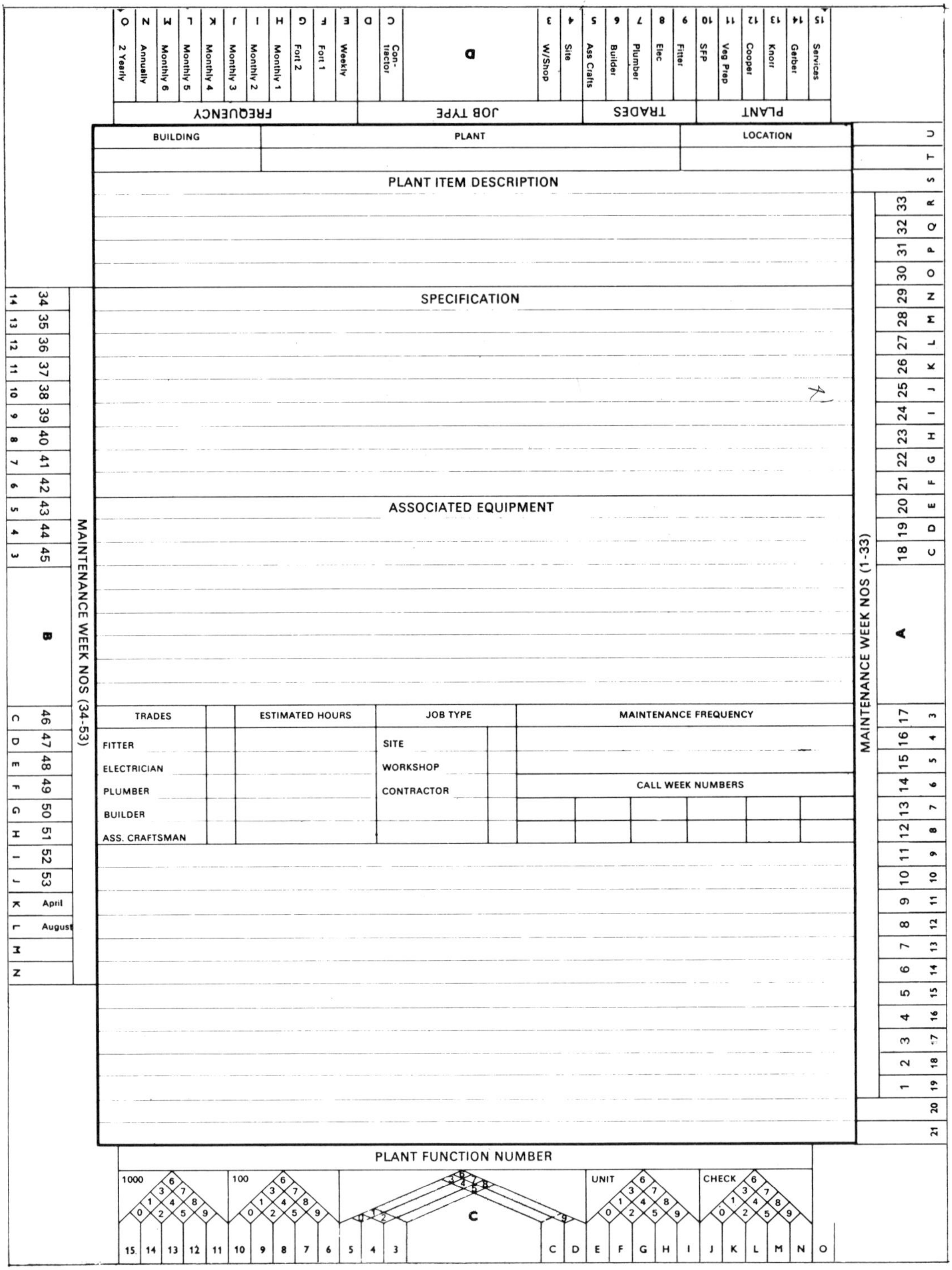

FREQUENCY

O 2 Yearly
N Annually
M Monthly 6
L Monthly 5
K Monthly 4
J Monthly 3
I Monthly 2
H Monthly 1
G Fort 2
F Fort 1
E Weekly

JOB TYPE

D
C Con-tractor

TRADES

3 W/Shop
4 Site
5 Ass Crafts
6 Builder
7 Plumber
8 Elec
9 Fitter

PLANT

10 SFP
11 Veg Prep
12 Cooper
13 Knorr
14 Gerber
15 Services

BUILDING   PLANT   LOCATION   U
T

PLANT ITEM DESCRIPTION   S

33 R
32 Q
31 P
30 O

SPECIFICATION

29 N
28 M
27 L
26 K
25 J
24 I
23 H
22 G
21 F
20 E
19 D
18 C

MAINTENANCE WEEK NOS (34-53)

34 14
35 13
36 12
37 11
38 10
39 9
40 8
41 7
42 6
43 5
44 4
45 3

B

ASSOCIATED EQUIPMENT

MAINTENANCE WEEK NOS (1-33)

A

17 3
16 4
15 5
14 6
13 7
12 8
11 9
10 10
9 11
8 12
7 13
6 14
5 15
4 16
3 17
2 18
1 19
20
21

46 C
47 D
48 E
49 F
50 G
51 H
52 I
53 J
April K
August L
M
N
Z

TRADES	ESTIMATED HOURS	JOB TYPE	MAINTENANCE FREQUENCY
FITTER		SITE	
ELECTRICIAN		WORKSHOP	
PLUMBER		CONTRACTOR	CALL WEEK NUMBERS
BUILDER			
ASS. CRAFTSMAN			

PLANT FUNCTION NUMBER

1000   100   C   UNIT   CHECK

15 14 13 12 11 10 9 8 7 6 5 4 3   C D E F G H I J K L M N O

Figure 4:1   Index card with edges coded for punching (Kalamazoo)

MECHANICAL CHECK LIST

FUNCTION NO.		
BUILDING NO.	IS PERMIT TO WORK REQUIRED	YES/NO
ITEM NO.	HAS MACHINE BEEN ISOLATED	YES/NO
FUNCTION NO.	MACHINE ISOLATED BY	DATE

DEPARTMENT

ITEM NO

ITEM DESCRIPTION

TRADES

HOURS

Site
W/S
Con

TYPE

DATE COMMENCE

RECTIFY ANY MINOR FAULTS FOUND AND REPORT MAJOR FAULTS ON REVERSE

MATERIAL SPARES REQUIRED

TIME

TIME TAKEN · SKILLED   UNSKILLED

COMPLETION

JOB INSPECTED AND DECLARED OPERATIONAL AND SAFE   DATE

Figure 4:1 — continued

Maker

Supplier

Description

Maker's number

New/second hand

Spares

Cost

Date

Drive

Insurance

Guarantee

Policy number | Renewable

Date | Location | Reference | Notes

H.P.	R.P.M.	Winding	Connected
Volts	Phase	Cycles per second	Amps per phase
AC or DC	Rotor amps	Rotor volts	Open circuit S.R. volts
Weight	Bearings	Frame size

Rating
Ordinary / Frequent — Intermittent / Continuous

Expected life — Years

Drawing number

Description | J F M A M J JY A S O N D

OOA | Location

Inspections

Category | Number

Figure 4:2   Plant and machinery record (electrical) (Kalamazoo)

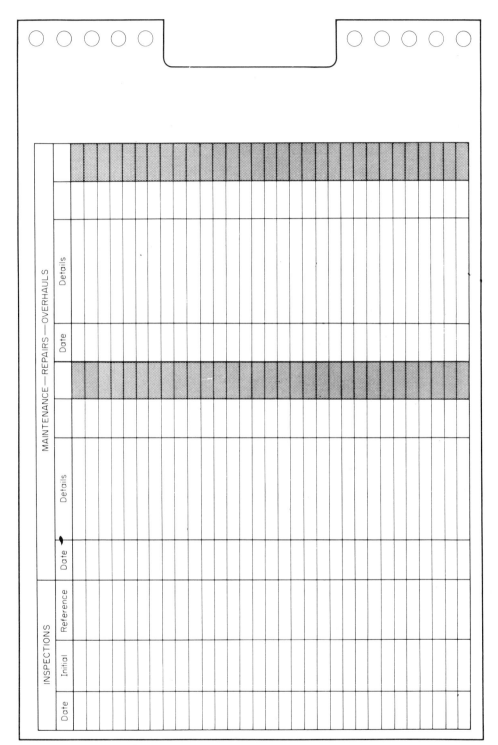

Figure 4:2 — contir ad

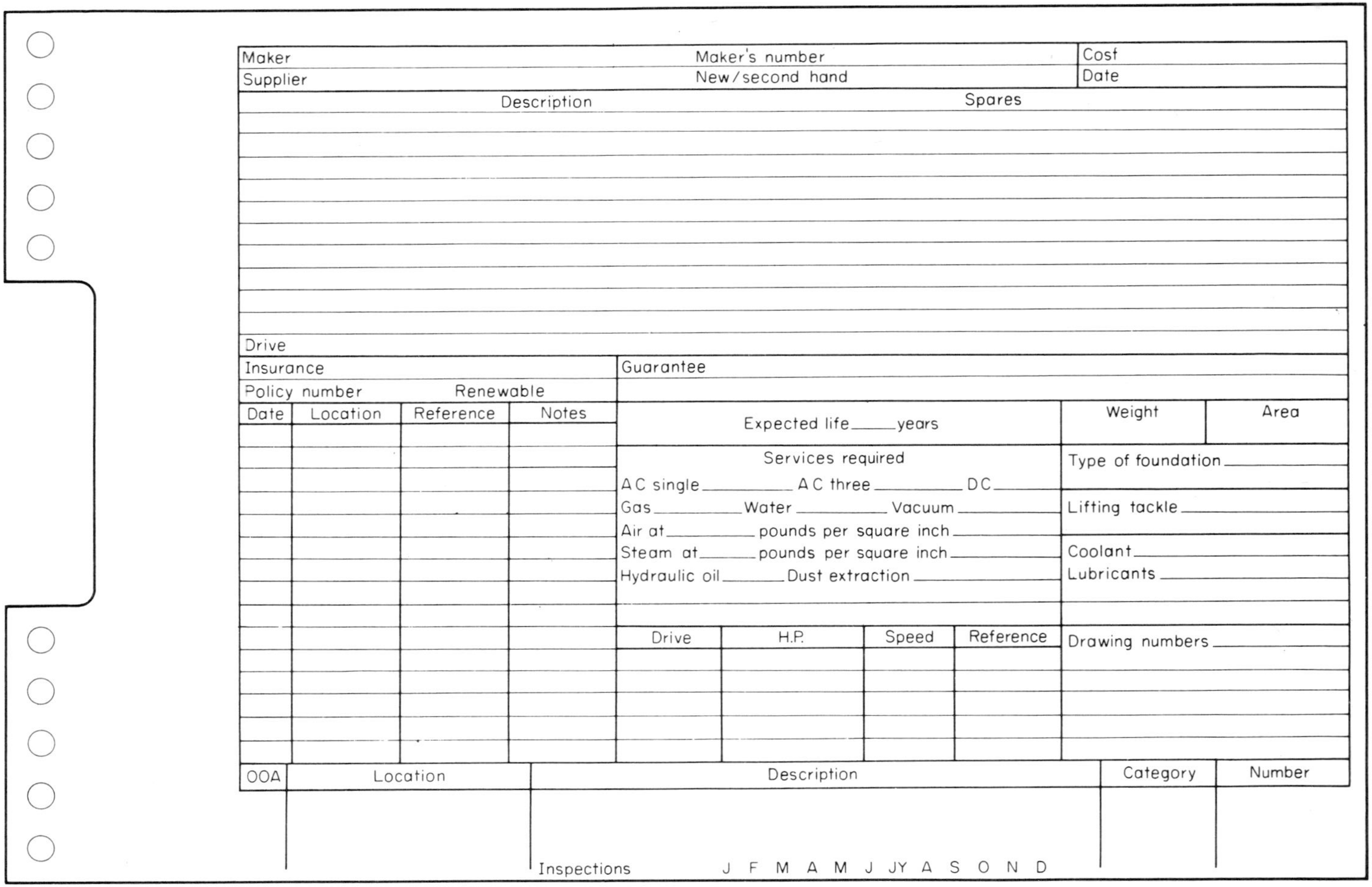

Maker | Maker's number | Cost
Supplier | New/second hand | Date

Description | Spares

Drive

Guarantee

Insurance

| Policy number | Renewable | | Notes |
| Date | Location | Reference | |

Expected life _____ years

Services required

AC single _____   AC three _____   DC _____
Gas _____   Water _____   Vacuum _____
Air at _____ pounds per square inch
Steam at _____ pounds per square inch
Hydraulic oil _____   Dust extraction _____

| Weight | Area |

Type of foundation _____
Lifting tackle _____
Coolant _____
Lubricants _____

| | H.P. | Speed | Reference | Drawing numbers |
| Drive | | | | |

Description

| Category | Number |

OOA   Location

Inspections   J F M A M J JY A S O N D

Figure 4:3   Plant and machinery record (mechanical) (Kalamazoo)

ITEM	Job Specification	Estimated Time	Frequency	Trade	Remarks
17	Check 1st Enrober Chain Drives		M	F	
18	Check Aftercooler Main Belt & Track		W	F	
19	Check Tracking Device		W	F	
20	Check Cooling Water Flow on Tables		W	F	
21	Check 2nd Enrober Choc Pump & Glands		W	F	
22	Check 2nd Enrober Bubble Eliminator		W	F	
23	Check 2nd Enrober Surge		W	F	
24	Check 2nd Enrober Temperature & Instruments		W	Lab.	
25	Check 2nd Enrober Jacket Water System		W	F	
26	Check 2nd Enrober Shake Mechanism		W	F	
27	Check 2nd Enrober Tailing Roller & Drive		W	F	
28	Check 2nd Enrober Wire Band		W	F	
29	Check 2nd Enrober Air Blower System		W	F	
30	Check Main Drive Unit		M	F	
31	Check Mult-Tier Cooler Main Chains		3M	F	
32	Check Multi-Tier Cooler Plaque Carriers		3M	F	
33	Check Multi-Tier Cooler 1st Transfer Device		3M	F	
34	Check Multi-Tier Cooler 2nd Transfer Device		3M	F	
35	Check Multi-Tier Cooler Temperature Controls		3M	F	
36	Remove Plaques for Cleaning & Check Rods		3M	F	
37	Check Drive of Take-off Unit		3M	F	
28	Check Magnetic Clutch		3M	F	
29	Check Safety Devices		W	F	

ENGINEERING MAINTENANCE   SHEET 1

Department: ENROBER   2nd Floor   Account No. 3945

Machine: No. 7 DOUBLE COVERER   Plant No.:

Daily	Weekly	2 Weekly	4 Weekly	12 Weekly	Yearly	
hrs	hrs	hrs	hrs	hrs		hrs
		O E	1234			

Figure 4:4   Page from maintenance diary with copy-strip inserts

This page may be photocopied without the overlay which contains estimated job times.

PLANT	TO BE LUBRICATED	METHOD	GRADE
	LATHES (Cont'd.)		
CENTRE LATHE Colchester Chipmaster 5 x 20	Headstock Gears and Bearings	Pump Circulated	HYSPIN 70
	Feed Gears	Oil Bath	HYSPIN 70
	Variable Speed Gear in Case	Oil Bath	HYSPIN 40
	Tailstock Bearings, Leadscrew, Saddle, and Traverse Shaft Bearings	Oil Nipples	MEDOS HEAVY
	Tool-post Cross and Bed Slides	Hand Oiled	MEDOS HEAVY
CENTRE LATHE Colchester Student	Headstock Gears and Bearings	Pump Circulated	HYSPIN 70
	Feed Gears	Oil Bath	PERFECTO MEDIUM
	Saddle Apron Gears	Hand Oiled	MEDOS HEAVY
	Tailstock Bearings, Leadscrew & Traverse Shaft Bearings, Toolpost Cross and Bed Slides	Hand Oiled & Oil Nipples	MEDOS HEAVY
CENTRE LATHE Churchill Redman	Headstock Gears and Bearings	Pump Circulated	MEDOS HEAVY
	Feed Gears	Oil Bath	MEDOS HEAVY
	Saddle Apron Gears	Oil Bath	MEDOS HEAVY
	Tailstock, Leadscrew, and Traverse Shaft Bearings, Tool- post Cross and Bed Slides	Hand Oiled & Oil Nipples	MEDOS HEAVY

Figure 4:5   Lubrication schedule using copy-strip system

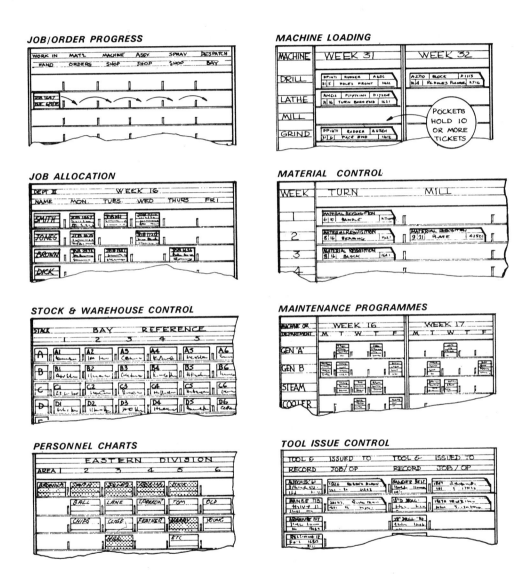

Figure 4:6   Typical uses for loading boards

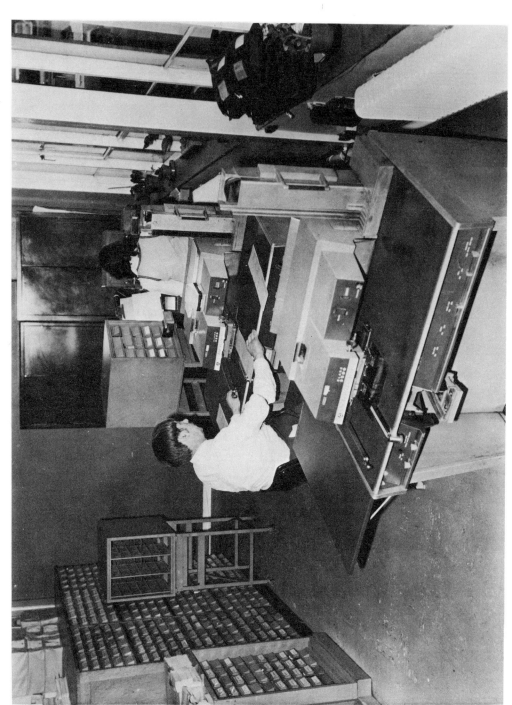

Figure 4:7   Installation for preparation of cards

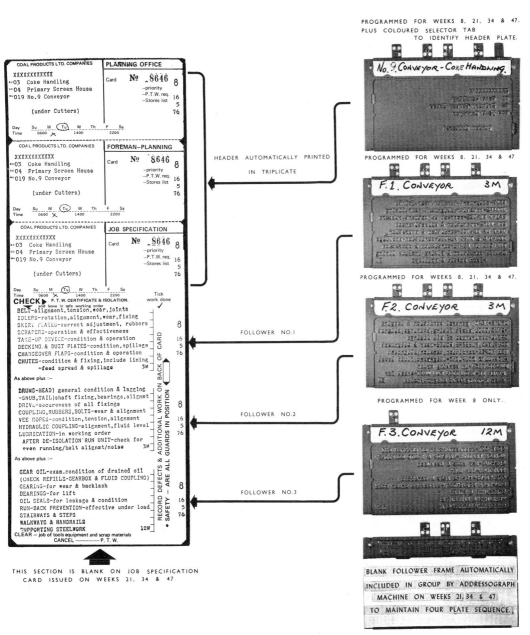

COAL PRODUCTS LTD. COMPANIES — **PLANNING OFFICE**

XXXXXXXXXXXXX
- ⁰⁰03 Coke Handling
- ⁰⁰04 Primary Screen House
- ⁰⁰019 No.9 Conveyor

(under Cutters)

Card № .8646   8
–priority
–P.T.W. req.   16
–Stores list   5
              76

Day Su M (Tu) W Th F Sa
Time   0600 X   1400   2200

No. 9. CONVEYOR - COKE HANDLING.

PROGRAMMED FOR WEEKS 8, 21, 34 & 47

HEADER AUTOMATICALLY PRINTED
IN TRIPLICATE

COAL PRODUCTS LTD. COMPANIES — **FOREMAN–PLANNING**

XXXXXXXXXXXXX
- ⁰⁰03 Coke Handling
- ⁰⁰04 Primary Screen House
- ⁰⁰019 No.9 Conveyor

(under Cutters)

Card № 8646   8
–priority
–P.T.W. req.   16
–Stores list   5
              76

Day Su M (Tu) W Th F Sa
Time   0600 X   1400   2200

F. 1. CONVEYOR   3M

PROGRAMMED FOR WEEKS 8, 21, 34 & 47.

COAL PRODUCTS LTD. COMPANIES — **JOB SPECIFICATION**

XXXXXXXXXXXXX
- ⁰⁰03 Coke Handling
- ⁰⁰04 Primary Screen House
- ⁰⁰019 No.9 Conveyor

(under Cutters)

Card № .8646   8
–priority
–P.T.W. req.   16
–Stores list   5
              76

Day Su M (Tu) W Th F Sa
Time   0600 X   1400   2200

Tick
work done
✓

CHECK ▶ P.T.W. CERTIFICATE & ISOLATION.
and leave in safe working order
BELT–alignment,tension,wear,joints
IDLERS–rotation,alignment,wear,fixing
SKIRT PLATES–correct adjustment, rubbers
SCRAPERS–operation & effectiveness
TAKE-UP DEVICE–condition & operation
DECKING & DUST PLATES–condition,spillage
CHANGEOVER FLAPS–condition & operation
CHUTES–condition & fixing,include lining
    –feed spread & spillage   3M

As above plus :–

DRUMS–HEAD) general condition & lagging
    –SNUB,TAIL)shaft fixing,bearings,alignmt
DRIVE–secureness of all fixings
COUPLING,RUBBERS,BOLTS–wear & alignment
VEE ROPES–condition,tension,alignment
HYDRAULIC COUPLING–alignment,fluid level
LUBRICATION–in working order
    AFTER DE-ISOLATION RUN UNIT–check for
    even running/belt alignmt/noise

As above plus :–

GEAR OIL–exam.condition of drained oil
(CHECK REFILLS–GEARBOX & FLUID COUPLING)
GEARING–for wear & backlash
BEARINGS–for lift
OIL SEALS–for leakage & condition
RUN-BACK PREVENTION–effective under load
STAIRWAYS & STEPS
WALKWAYS & HANDRAILS
SUPPORTING STEELWORK   12M
CLEAR – job of tools equipment and scrap materials
        CANCEL ------------- P. T. W.

8
16
5
76

8
16
5
76

8
16
5
76

RECORD DEFECTS & ADDITIONAL WORK ON BACK OF CARD
• SAFETY – ARE ALL GUARDS IN POSITION

FOLLOWER NO.1

FOLLOWER NO.2

FOLLOWER NO.3

F.2. CONVEYOR   3M

PROGRAMMED FOR WEEKS 8, 21, 34 & 47.

PROGRAMMED FOR WEEK 8 ONLY.

F.3. CONVEYOR   12M

THIS SECTION IS BLANK ON JOB SPECIFICATION
CARD ISSUED ON WEEKS 21, 34 & 47

BLANK FOLLOWER FRAME AUTOMATICALLY
INCLUDED IN GROUP BY ADDRESSOGRAPH
MACHINE ON WEEKS 21, 34 & 47
TO MAINTAIN FOUR PLATE SEQUENCE.

Figure 4:8   Typical card with printing plates

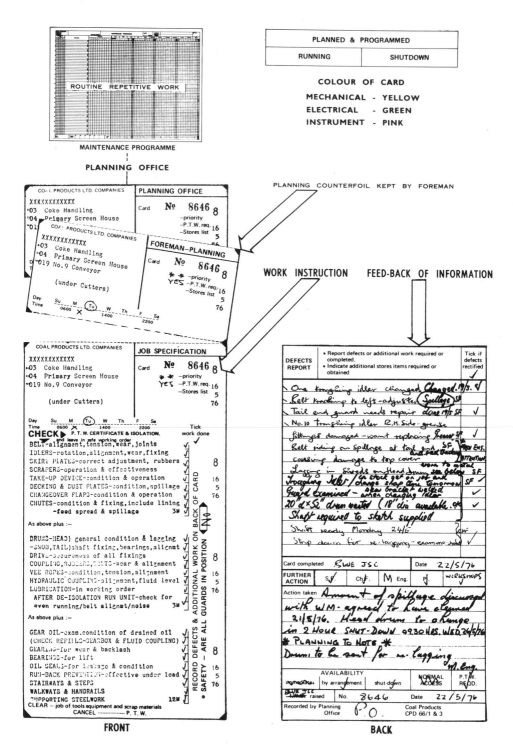

Figure 4:9   Card system for routine maintenance

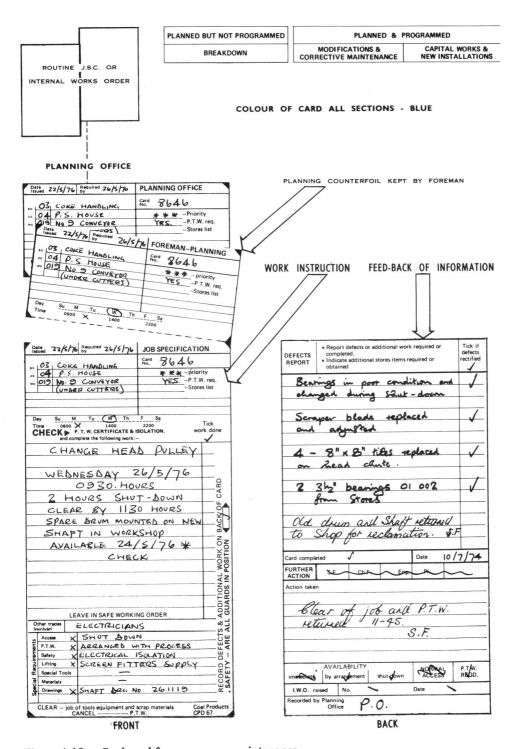

Figure 4:10   Card used for emergency maintenance

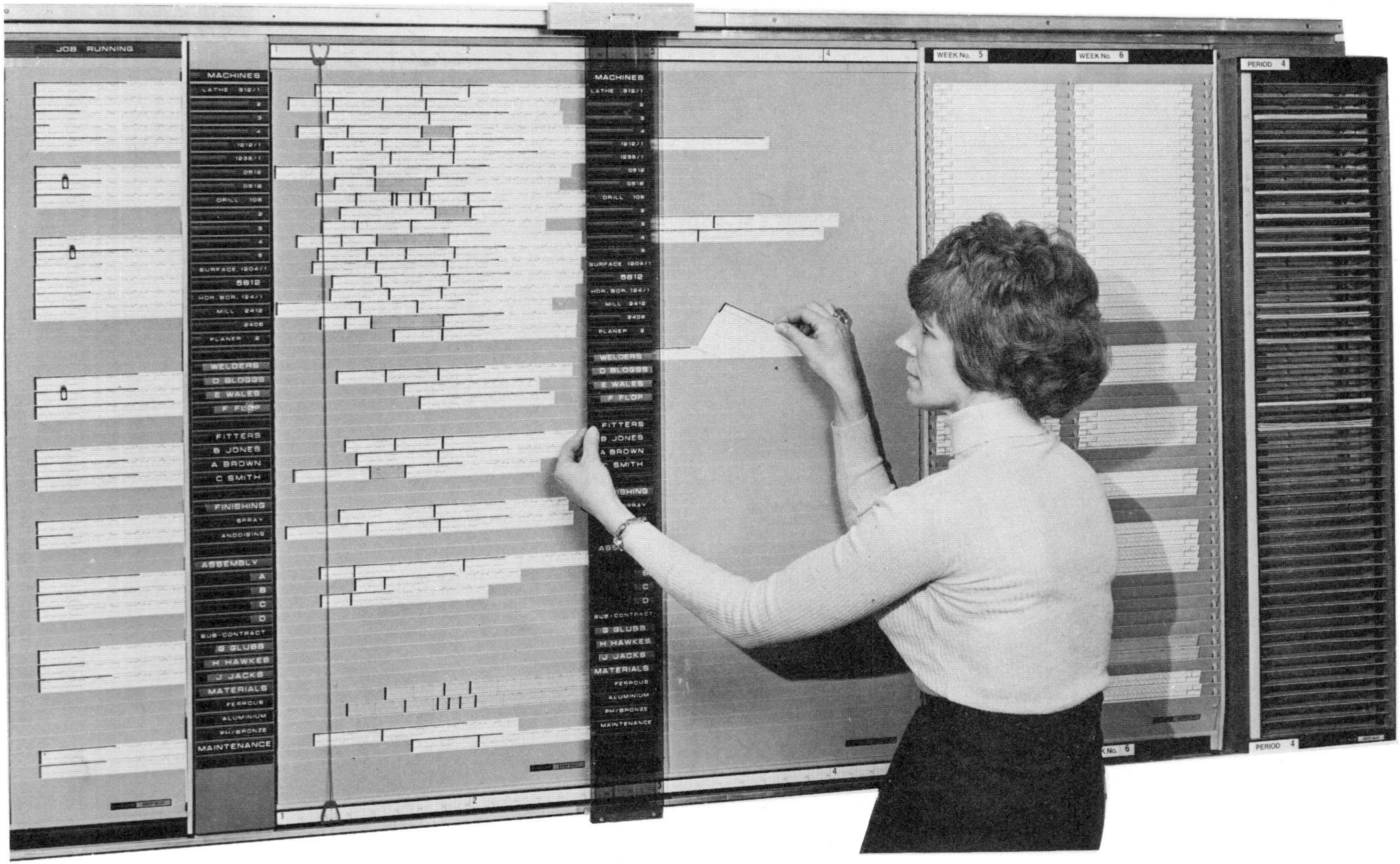

Figure 4:11   Planning boards for Work Programming

Figure 4:11 — continued

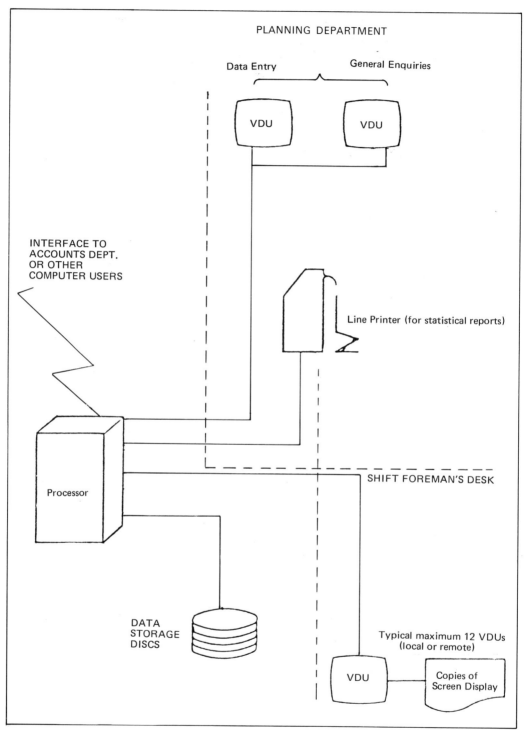

Figure 4:12   Mini-computer system for maintenance control

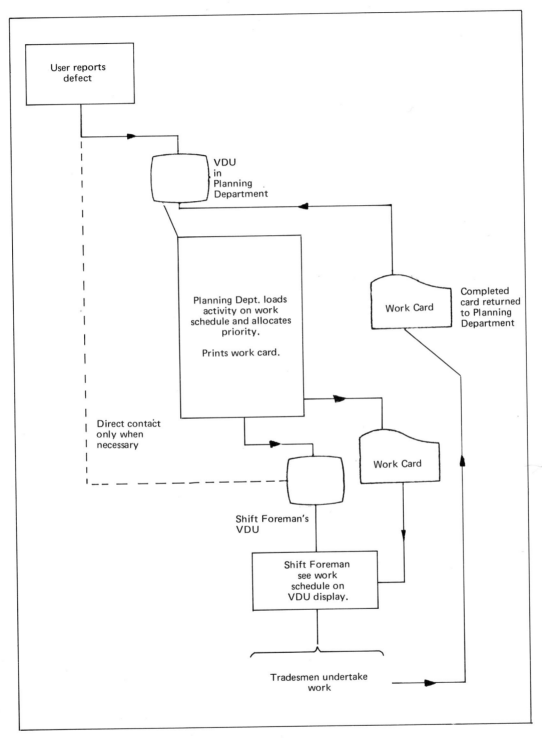

Figure 4:13   Activity flow-chart for routine maintenance

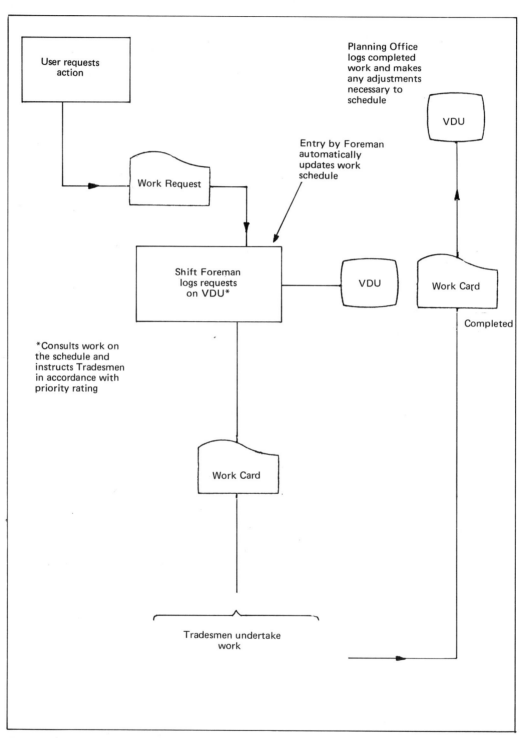

Figure 4:14   Activity flow-chart for emergency maintenance

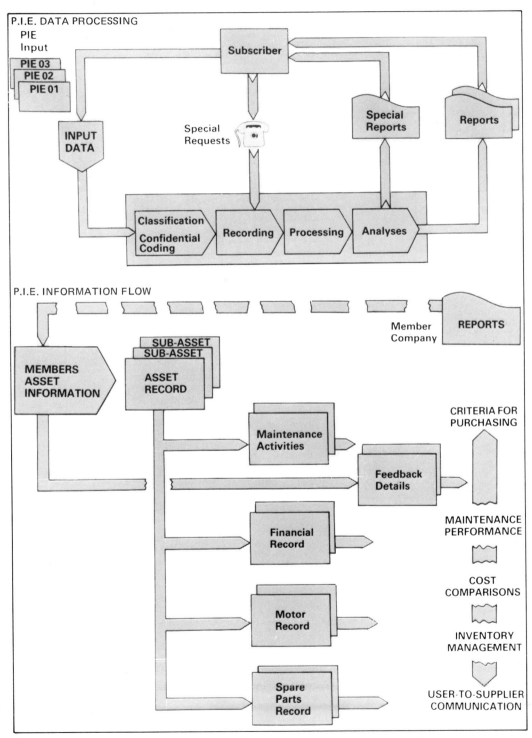

Figure 4:15   Plant information exchange (P.I.E.)

Figure 4:16　Record card for history and feedback

Feedback Card No. 9 0

Company

Asset No.　Name

Location　Area

Card No.	Item No.	Date	Feedback Information (narrative)	FEEDBACK REFERENCES			ACTION
				A	B C		YES NO

Date Completed:—　Completed by:—

TOTAL MAINTENANCE SYSTEMS

© Comprehensive Maintenance Services Ltd. P.O. Box 257 West Byfleet KT14 6AZ Printed in England 1978

5

Maintenance
Management and Personnel

The government report on maintenance stated the relationship between industrial productivity and the proper selection and training of maintenance personnel. 'Investment in costly machinery without comparable investment in competent people is poor management.' This chapter looks at the human aspects and at the communication channels both within and from the maintenance department.

The Maintenance Manager

Maintenance managers range from promoted members of the maintenance staff to specially recruited professional managers. Their qualifications range from Ordinary National Certificate to degree standard and many are chartered engineers. A number of successful maintenance managers have come from engineer/officer posts in the services. The sizes of departments administered range from 6 to 500 personnel with additional responsibilities for a wide range of contract personnel employed on work ranging from window cleaning to capital projects. In addition to membership of the engineering institution associated with their individual discipline, many maintenance managers are members of the Institution of Plant Engineers and members of local maintenance associations which provide facilities for technical and social gatherings. These area associations are linked through the British Council of Maintenance Associations to an international body, the European Federation of National Maintenance Societies.

Within a particular company the maintenance manager may be responsible to the directors, to the works manager or to the chief engineer. In some companies the chief engineer also acts as maintenance manager. The actual title held by the manager of the maintenance function may be maintenance manager, chief engineer, works engineer, plant engineer, plant manager, manager of technical services, engineering manager, etc. Within a group of companies or a group of factories each installation may have a works engineer or maintenance manager, reporting partly to the local management and also to a head office manager known as chief engineer or engineering manager. Some typical hierarchies are described later.

Typical functions of a chief engineer will include:

1 Responsibility for the plant maintenance department.
2 Responsibility for buildings and services maintenance.
3 Responsibility for workshops (repairs, overhauls, welding, retooling, spares manufacture).
4 Planning and supervision of capital work (construction, installation, removals, commissioning).
5 Planning of utilities (steam, electricity, oil, air, waste, effluent, etc.).
6 Responsibility for plant engineering (transport, instrumentation, machines, control systems, modifications, modernization, replacement policies, operational developments).
7 Fire precautions, safety, technical personnel, in-plant research and development, security, staff facilities, etc.

Management Hierarchies

Some typical management hierarchies appear below.

(1)   Chief engineer (Group level)

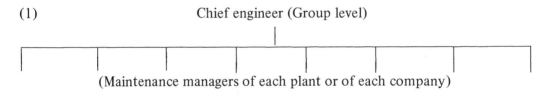

(Maintenance managers of each plant or of each company)

(2)   Group technical director

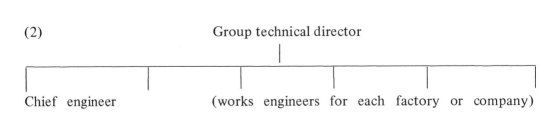

Chief engineer   (works engineers for each factory or company)

In the above structure the chief engineer will be responsible for technical development, R and D, new plant and improved services.

(3)

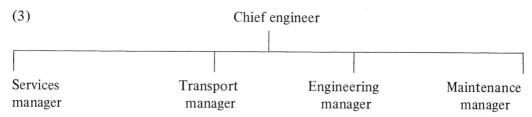

Here, the maintenance manager's responsibility is limited to the maintenance function for the plant itself. The services manager attends to buildings and utilities, with the engineering manager responsible for plant procurement, plant engineering and technical development.

(4)

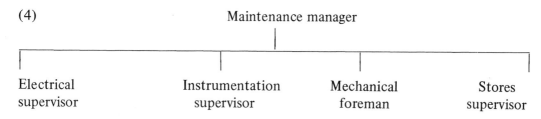

The basic divisions of maintenance supervision are often in terms of trade skills. If three shifts are worked these positions may be repeated on each shift or each shift may have chargehands reporting to the above supervisors in each of the disciplines.

(5)

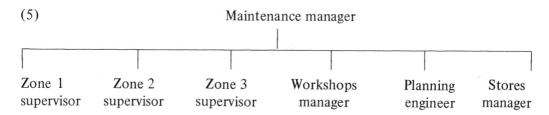

In example (5) the plant is split on a zonal basis, each zone supervisor having foremen or chargehands in the various trade groups to supervise his zone labour force. Central workshops are provided for the overhaul and repair work, also for spare parts refurbishing or spares manufacture. Decentralization has much to recommend it if there is a requirement for localized expertise with rapid availability in the various sectors of the plant. This also helps to develop trust and understanding between operatives and their local maintenance personnel.

(6)

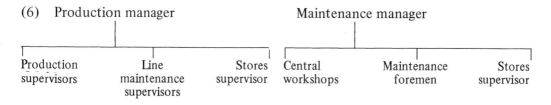

In many process plants the line maintenance (calibration, minor repairs, preventive maintenance, lubrication, etc.) is the responsibility of the production department which has a separate multidisciplined team of maintenance personnel. This facilitates production/maintenance liaison but can lead to duplication of personnel and facilities (for example, stores).

(7)

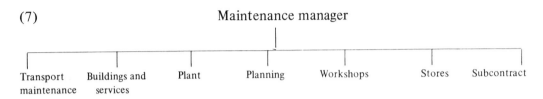

It is important to remember the value of contract services, not only on new projects work but also for preventive maintenance routines, plant inspections, overhaul and repair work, annual shutdown maintenance, commissioning and modifications.

The astute plant manager will not staff his department to the maximum but will utilize perhaps 10 per cent of contract labour to provide the necessary flexibility in his labour force. In addition, contract labour is useful for services such as window cleaning and to augment the regular labour force during plant shutdown for overhaul. In a medium-to-large maintenance or plant engineering department it may be advisable to appoint a subcontracts supervisor responsible directly to the maintenance manager or chief engineer.

(8)

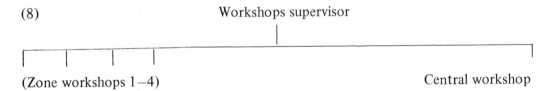

In a large plant or in a group of factories under common administration it may be convenient to establish local workshops to undertake small tasks or emergency work with a feedback of major tasks, complex tasks or continuous work to the central workshops. In this situation chargehands or supervisors are required to plan and coordinate the work flow, reporting to the workshops supervisor. These workshops have the advantage of providing fast-access local facilities and also standby work for zoned personnel. However, the planning and coordination aspects must be controlled. The engineering stores may also be zoned to provide a fast local service to zone personnel.

(9) Maintenance manager

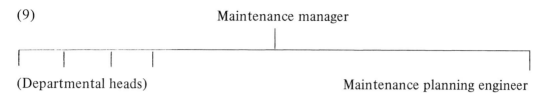

(Departmental heads)   Maintenance planning engineer

Whatever the structure of the maintenance department, the planning engineer must have direct access to the manager. Where the planned system is set up by a consultant, the operator of the system (engineer or clerk) also requires direct access to the manager.

Interdepartmental Communication

Communication and feedback are important elements of the terotechnology system. The maintenance manager, as a member of the management team of the company, will communicate with fellow managers as follows:

Communication	With	Feedback
	Production manager	
Maintenance programme		Production programme
Shutdown requirements		Plant availability for maintenance
Technical suggestions		Production requirements
Operating defects		Maintenance defects
Plant replacement requests		Budgetary implications
Spares policies and costs		Production department comments
	Chief engineer	
Technical suggestions		Engineer's comments
Plant renewal suggestions		Financial/technical comments
Plant performance reports		Modification procedures
For new installations:		
Manning proposals		Details of all proposed new
Technical suggestions		installations
Standardization reports		
Maintenance programme summaries		Comments on summaries
Costing and performance statistics		Comments on statistics
	Accounts department	
Expenditure		Cost summaries
Budgetary proposals		Budget comparisons
Projects expenditure		Projects spending rates
Stock issues		Materials costs
Labour utilization		Manpower costs

(continued overleaf)

Communication	With	Feedback
	Personnel department	
Labour requirements		Labour availability
Surplus labour		Rundown proposals
Salary proposals		Company policy
Safety activities		Safety policies
Staff facilities		Requirements

Other departments in accordance with the company hierarchy.

Operations/Maintenance Liaison

NOTE: The words 'operator' and 'user' are used in the general sense here because these remarks apply to buildings and plant, whether industrial, commercial or public assets. In a factory the user is a member of the production team, in a hotel the user may be the manager or the chef, in a hospital the administrator or a senior member of the medical team.

Effective communication with the operator or user is necessary at all levels in the maintenance hierarchy. For example, the maintenance planning staff have to liaise with the operations planners not only on the initial programme but also on a regular basis to discuss:

1   Requests for service by the users.
2   Work postponed as a result of emergency demands on maintenance personnel.
3   Work delayed by changed operational requirements for the assets.
4   Work held over because spares, materials or other essential items are not available.

These faults often give rise to extensive changes of schedule.

At lower levels direct contact between the maintenance and the user includes:

1   Issue of requests for services (calibration, adjustment, repair, etc.) by operations supervisors.
2   Regular inspections of running plant by the maintenance personnel.
3   Feedback on operating conditions by the operatives.
4   Advice on technical matters by maintenance personnel.
5   Joint discussions on variations in the way the asset is used, and other facets of effective performance from the man and/or the machine.

In connection with the last item, it is important to note the reduction in efficiency which can result from strained operations/maintenance worker relationships. Effective communication between these two groups encourages:

1   A degree of operator fault diagnosis, reducing the number of calls for service.
2   Improved operator appreciation of technical features of machinery.
3   Improved handling of machine records.
4   Identification of variations in the input materials, or in environmental states which may adversely affect machinery.
5   Cooperation on fault-finding and repair.
6   A higher standard of cleanliness for the asset and its environs.

Plant Development/Maintenance Liaison

Even when the plant development department and the plant maintenance department are controlled by the same person there can be technical communication gaps which are expensive and time consuming to bridge. Typical information flows between the two departments are listed below:

Plant development manager to maintenance manager

1   Proposals for new installations or machines.
2   Lists of machines and components before procurement action is finalized.
3   Spares recommendations.
4   Manning requirements.
5   Plant modification proposals.
6   Requests for maintenance policies on plant.
7   Advance drawings, installation and commissioning procedures.
8   Maintenance manuals, spares lists, lubrication plans.

Maintenance manager to plant development manager

1   Comments on proposed new installations from installation and maintenance viewpoints.
2   Suggestions for standardization of machines and components.
3   Proposals for spares rationalization and details of spares already held.
4   Manning proposals.
5   Comments on maintainability aspects.
6   Suggestions for monitoring facilities, for replacement policies, access, handling and fault diagnosis.
7   Detail comments on installation requirements.
8   Specification of information requirements.

The cost of installation, the cost of spares and maintenance, the standing investment in spares, the downtime during fault-finding and repair, and the life expectancy of the plant can all benefit from increased designer/user cooperation. See Chapter 10 'Procurement' for details of buyer/vendor relationships when external plant vendors are used.

Maintenance Planning Engineer

The maintenance planner can be an in-plant engineer, or a temporary engineer supplied by a consultancy or service organization. The maintenance planner must be capable of:

1   Extracting maintenance schedules from vendor manuals to form the basis of a master maintenance schedule.
2   Obtaining additional technical information so that the schedule is complete.
3   Making his own assessment of the daily, weekly and other activities necessary for an asset, working from his own experience and a study of the asset, its drawings, and specifications.

Human Factors

It is quite possible to think of maintenance personnel as craftsmen and to forget that they have the same human factors to contend with as production operators, who are often made the subject of human-factor studies. Moreover the dependence upon the maintenance man brought about by economic developments and also the spread of automation is increasing the importance of recognition of these factors and the introduction of communication, control, and working conditions which provide the best situation for job satisfaction, contentment, and effective working by the maintenance staff. The increasing importance of the maintenance man in the automated plant situation is shown by an analysis of the labour force employed on one assembly line in a factory where in the 1960s the labour force consisted of 22 operators and one part-time maintenance man, whereas in the 1970s on the same line the labour force was five operators and nine full-time maintenance men. Moreover, the introduction of automation had produced a continuous process line in which the breakdown of any one machine brings the whole line to a halt and manual by-pass arrangements are no longer possible.

Among the factors attracting labour to the maintenance department are the following:

1   Technical achievement coupled with a sense of superiority over operators on the production line.
2   Pride in and the desire to maintain trade skills which quickly decline if more remunerative and less-technical work is undertaken.
3   Security, which has in the past been heightened by the fact that in so many plants where redundancies have occurred the force least affected is that within the maintenance department.
4   A tendency to follow the technical line existing in a family in which the members have always been associated with maintenance and repair work.

5   The freedom of movement that comes with working in the maintenance department, whereby a considerable change of job location is possible within a given installation and the type of boredom associated with single-station operative work is avoided.

6   Opportunities for advancement — although these tended to be limited in the past with perhaps 20 maintenance men reporting to one foreman, there are now increasing opportunities for promotion particularly where further study can lead to a multi-discipline post in which the maintenance man is completely responsible for a considerable section of plant — crossing the demarcation borders which have divided electrical work, mechanical work, hydraulic work, etc.

The full significance of this last point has not yet been recognized by many bodies concerned with training, personnel development and labour relations within the maintenance industry.

Some of the factors which inhibit recruitment to the maintenance labour force or cause trained maintenance men to leave and seek other opportunities are outlined below.

Weekend working.   If maintenance is not adequately planned it is possible for the whole of the overhaul and repair work to become weekend work and this tends to make the maintenance men a race apart, working at the weekend when other less skilled men are attending social functions with their wives and children. In many installations it has been necessary to introduce seven-day working systems with stoppages for maintenance being arranged on various days in successive weeks so that the dependence on Saturday and Sunday working is reduced.

Salary conditions.   The introduction of work study schemes has enabled many maintenance workers to earn higher salaries and may well have resulted in higher output and increased stability of the labour force in some plant installations. However, there are problems with the introduction of work study techniques and these have been referred to elsewhere. Probably the most effective maintenance department is that in which a standing bonus is allowed and is made relevant to the actual performance of the maintenance department in terms of maintaining utlization rather than on a complicated system of work measurement which has to be adjusted to allow for much of the work being of an unplanned nature.

Frustration.   The maintenance man has often been neglected in time past in terms of organization, control, training, technical information, etc., and considerable job frustration has been a feature of the maintenance department, causing many trained maintenance men to seek other employment. The provision of accurate and comprehensive technical information, the provision of a good support organization providing tools and spares and other materials, the provision of a control system which ensures that all work is directed towards goals which can be seen to be effective, reduces frustration and enhances job satisfaction in the maintenance department.

Working conditions.   In many established installations it has been possible to achieve a much better labour situation in the maintenance department by upgrading the accommodation provided (in many factories the maintenance department has been sited on spare ground at the rear of the plant), by providing protective clothing, and by providing rest rooms, clothes lockers, showers and other aids to personal wellbeing.

The maintenance man, his motivations, his philosophies and his training and development, have not been given the attention in recent years that has been given to the production operative, the office worker, and workers in other industrial labour groups.   It is obviously time for a serious study of this in the hope that this will produce the benefits required without excessive recourse to work study and other incentive methods which can tend to reduce the long-term standing of the maintenance man as a professional technician whose work is essential to assets management and the quality of whose work is very much a matter of personal skill and application.

Communication

Communication channels in the maintenance department are both vertical (management/man) and horizontal (man/man).   There is also the clear requirement for effective communication of technical information regarding the maintenance and repair of the buildings, services, plant and machines.

Vertical communication should be provided for by the paperwork of the planning and control system, with work instructions being issued to staff as a result of maintenance policies agreed at management level.   The maintenance control systems described in this book provide for this, including the notification of appropriate operations and stores personnel.   In the reverse direction information regarding work done, materials used, time spent, work held over and technical information (including requests for corrective maintenance) is provided by staff.   This flow of feedback information is essential for costing, recording and future planning.

Horizontal communication in many maintenance departments is inadequate. Failures by personnel in different trade groups, even in the same trade groups, to exchange information are commonplace.   The lack of training, particularly induction training for new maintenance personnel, is a contributory factor.   In particular, the retention of specific knowledge of a machine by a worker can add considerable downtime when another maintenance man, possibly on another shift, faces a similar situation.   When defect reports are used to bridge this gap it is essential that information recorded is disseminated to the relevant personnel.

Another aspect of technical communication in the maintenance department is the provision of adequate technical manuals or other working instructions. (The performance of many plant vendors in this connection leaves much to be desired.) Very often technical manuals arrive long after commissioning (because they have been written by the design engineers who wait until the task is complete before preparing the technical manuals), frequently no manuals at all are supplied, and it is almost unknown for technical manuals to be completely user-oriented. Technical manuals are expensive because technical writers compile them and technical illustrators provide the pictures but they reduce downtime, safeguard vital plant, reduce maintenance costs, and are a major factor in providing job satisfaction for maintenance labour. In recent years a further sophistication has been apparent in some areas in that a maintenance philosophy for particular equipment has been developed at the design stage and this philosophy has been followed through in the preparation of technical manuals, preparation of fault diagnosis routines, provision of spare parts, etc. However, in many of the products supplied by plant vendors there is still little evidence of this forward thinking. The problems of obtaining adequate product support (technical manuals, spares lists, maintenance schedules, and operator and engineer training aids) are dealt with in the section dealing with procurements.

The importance of technical communication in this respect is now seen by many maintenance managers who allocate budgets for the retrospective preparation of this information for plant already in service. This will be dealt with under 'Maintenance Improvement' (Chapter 7).

Labour Turnover in the Maintenance Department

Initially, in any plant installation, it can be expected that a high degree of stability will exist within the maintenance labour force because the new equipment and the technical challenge it creates will encourage the pride in technical ability which is a feature of craftsman behaviour. However, the style of management and the type of organization selected for the maintenance department will affect the continuance of a stable situation more than any other factor. Studies have shown annual turnovers of 25 per cent in male labour in highly industrialized areas and the cost of this to a company can represent more than 1 per cent of the annual sales value. In the maintenance department labour turnover costs include:

1   Administration costs.
2   Advertising costs.
3   Familiarization costs for new staff.
4   Increased fault finding and repair time costs.
5   Loss of production during training.
6   Cost of waste, scrap or repairs.

7   Increased supervision costs.
8   Overtime charges by other staff handling additional work.

Many tradesmen enter the maintenance field and derive great satisfaction from the skilful servicing and repair of the plant on which the mere operators depend for their living. However, the high wages attained by certain semi-technical operators in the process plants, automobile factories, etc., can create a drain on the maintenance departments of industry as skilled tradesmen leave their trade to join a production line and share in the bonuses which are available from mass-production work. Examples have occurred in the automobile servicing industry where garages have been denuded of skilled maintenance mechanics who have taken to factory work for considerably higher salaries. If this type of labour turnover is to be avoided it is essential that training opportunities, excellent industrial relations, pride in good workmanship, and job satisfaction are developed in the maintenance department.

6

Training

Sufficient information is available from the official teaching bodies, or from the various organizations offering courses and seminars, for the maintenance manager wishing to select additional standard training for members of his staff. This chapter is therefore devoted to reminders of special training which may be undertaken as part of a maintenance improvement programme.

Maintenance Management

The chapter titles of this book provide a useful guide to the range of subjects making up an effective training or refresher course for managers of the maintenance function. The following list contains the minimum acceptable number of subjects to form the syllabus of a maintenance management course.

Maintenance Engineering. Description – objectives – development – vital aspects – hierarchies – safety.
Personnel. Types and grades – training – qualifications.
Maintenance Support: Control systems – records – documentation – stores – equipment (tools, etc.) – workshops – transport – maintenance aids (monitoring, etc.) – waste disposal.
Communication. Technical communication with staff – communication with other departments.
Maintenance Improvement. Preventive maintenance reviews – overhaul planning – technical information – fault diagnosis and repair – performance analyses – stock control.
Manpower Utilization. Resourcing – supervision – communication – planning –

work measurement — productivity — incentives — feedback.

Costing and Budgeting.   Costing — forecasting — accounting methods — budgeting — feedback.

Procurement.   New plant — capital works — designer liaison — product support — spares rationalization — subcontracting — plant replacement — services contracts and tariffs.

Safety Appreciation

The pattern of safety in a particular installation is established during the design and installation phase and is further influenced during subsequent operation and maintenance. Good design and correct installation can be ensured during commissioning (particularly if reliable commissioning consultants are employed) and the operation of a planned maintenance system is a constant safeguard during operation. Items to be considered on new-plant safety courses are listed below:

Planned safety
1   Good layout providing access, egress, etc.
2   Careful planning of services.
3   Route planning for machine deliveries.
4   Environmental planning — heat, light, air, etc.
5   Scaffolding, ladders, etc. provisioning.
6   Interpreters for installation of foreign plant.
7   Clear definitions of responsibility and management.
8   Specification of requirements for interlocks, guards, etc. on plant.

Installation
1   Delivery check for requirement 8, above.
2   Installation and operating instructions availability.
3   Competent supervision for plant handling.
4   Isolation of services during installation.
5   Prohibition of temporary service connections.
6   Fire and glare protection when welding.

Commissioning
1   Specification and procedure agreed in advance.
2   No connection of services until approved.
3   Slow-speed start with full check on safety features.
4   All overload devices calibrated.
5   Control and shutdown procedures verified.
6   Working positions and visibility checked.
7   Safety training given.

Planned maintenance

1   Maintenance information available.
2   Maintenance planning introduced.
3   Safety shutdowns agreed.
4   Priorities for maintenance of safety features.
5   Statutory tests performed to schedule.
6   Correct tools and access equipment supplied.
7   Ancillary equipment maintained also.

Technical Communication for Plant Designers

Many excellent designers lack communication ability and much useful information is unrecorded for maintenance purposes. Successful courses are run to improve this situation in the design offices of leading companies, and can be extended to in-plant development departments.

Typical course contents include:

1   Instruction in technical writing.
2   Information on drawing and graphic techniques.
3   The structuring of information.
4   The identification and coding of parts and spares.
5   Presentation of technical information.
6   Printing and other reproduction techniques.
7   Procurement of specialist services.

The course objectives are:

1   To develop provision of standard and comprehensive operating and mainten-
     ance information.
2   To reduce designer involvement in commissioning.
3   To encourage modification recording.
4   To reduce designer involvement in repair and servicing activity.
5   To encourage maintainability analysis during design recording.

Engineering Appreciation for Operations Managers

Significant improvements in the operation and maintenance of productive plant are obtained when operations managers are provided with selected information on maintenance and engineering services. The contents of a typical course are outlined below:—

The engineering function. Introduction to terminology, organization plan, etc. Definition of production/engineering communications. Operator/maintainer relationships. Improving productivity.

Plant management.   General organization and administration. Objectives. Identification of requirements, critical plant areas, etc.

Planned maintenance.   Principles, benefits and objectives. Control system. Documentation. Records. Planned overhaul. Lubrication.

Maintenance support.   Technical manuals. Tools. Spares. Contractors.

Capital projects.   Management of new projects, alterations, etc.

Breakdown and repair.   Fault diagnosis. Maintainability. Failure reports. Corrective maintenance. Documentation/event sequences.

Budgeting.   Components of budget. Preparation. Contingencies.

Costing.   Accounts codes. Overhead allocations. Cost areas.

Engineering stores.   Control and accounting procedures. Rationalization.

Personnel.   Trade groups. Staff agreements. Productivity. Safety.

Supplies and services.   Oil, gas, electricity, water regulations. Economics. Tariffs.

Special plant groups.   Steam raising plant. Motors and drives. Controls and instrumentation.

Transport.   (internal/external) Selection. Replacement. Safety. Maintenance.

Statutory requirements.   Safety. Insurance. Cranes and hoists. Boilers. Noise control. Fire protection. Antipollution. Waste and effluent disposal.

The above syllabus provides a comprehensive picture of the work of the maintenance department. The depth of treatment can be reduced to provide a course of acceptable length.

Staff Development Courses

The following list of courses is given as a reminder for maintenance managers seeking to develop incoming or existing staff members as a maintenance improvement plan.

Induction training

New entries to the maintenance department can benefit from an induction course, designed to speed their adoption of the best working methods and of the approved communication channels. Typical subjects to be included are:

1   Welfare and personnel functions (if not already dealt with).

2 Management hierarchies and family trees.
3 Documentation and paperwork.
4 Technical information, manuals, drawings, etc.
5 Liaison with production.
6 Stores, test gear and access equipment procedures.
7 Planned maintenance procedures and routes.

Repair technician courses

In a suitable environment repair technicians may be trained to specialize in repair and servicing of vital machines, particularly when multidiscipline working is necessary. Training begins with the development of suitable charts, manuals, etc. and a thorough understanding of engineering drawings and other available information. Training in the various disciplines is then necessary followed by analysis of fault-finding and repair work across the disciplines.

In some plants this has been extended to give, for example, electrical training to fitters and mechanical training to electricians. The objectives of the courses must include (*a*) the development of a thorough understanding of the machines and (*b*) a reduction of the time-wasting interface problems between trade skill groups.

Fault diagnosis training

Fault-finding and repair training may be general or specific in nature. General training courses include:

1 Refresher lectures on basic disciplines.
2 Use of drawings, recognition of symbols.
3 Development of fault diagnosis methods.
4 Use of charts and other aids.

When training on specific machines is given it is usual to prepare fault-finding charts (see Chapter 8) as a first step and then to instruct in their use.

Advanced skills training

Courses within this category may be selected to improve the performance of existing staff in fault-finding and repair or in coping with new plant employing new or advanced control or instrumentation techniques. Typical examples are:

Simple programming course. For electronic technicians engaged in the maintenance of plant which is computer controlled and on which the first line of repair involves the use of test programs.

Hydraulic or pneumatic systems training. For use where the introduction of these systems, or the use of more complex systems, is causing repair delays related to inexperience.

Electronic appreciation courses for electricians. These have been applied successfully in industries where the basic product (e.g. office machinery) now operates
electronically.

Systems appreciation training. Courses designed to encourage system thinking in
technicians called upon to maintain systemized plant rather than individual
machines.

Introduction to Computers

When computer systems are considered for asset management applications it is
essential to prepare staff at all levels by suitable introductory courses. This applies
not only to asset managers and maintenance managers but also to supervisors,
foremen and trades union representatives. Managers and supervisors from other
departments affected by the computer system should also be informed. Course
contents should include:

1   Brief history of computers.
2   Introduction to computer terminology.
3   Why computers are used.
4   The computer as an aid to maintenance.
5   The computer in feedback analysis.

Introduction to Terotechnology

The application of terotechnology and life cycle costing techniques to assets
management demands an understanding of these concepts not only in the maintenance department but in associated departments of an organization or company.
Training programmes must not only introduce these subjects but also provide
guidance on those aspects whose improvement is an essential part of the overall plan.
Typical of these aspects are communication, computerization and health and safety.
Examples of terotechnology training programmes follow:—

Terotechnology for Project Managers

Terotechnology
    The Terotechnology System
Economics
    Life Cycle Costing
    Financial Techniques
    Costs Management

Project Management
Study Phase
Evaluation Phase
Implementation Phase
Handover Phase
Additional Subjects (as required)
Contracts and Buying
Personnel Management
Operations Management
Maintenance Management
Communication
Information Systems
Technical Communication and Feedback
Training Programmes
Computers
Introduction to Computers
Applications for Computers
Health and Safety

Terotechnology for Operations Managers

Terotechnology
The Terotechnology System
Life Cycle Costs
Initial Costs
Operating Costs
Downtime Costs
Maintenance
The Maintenance Organization
Preventive Maintenance
Operator/Maintainer Liaison
Statutory Requirements
Computers in Maintenance Management
Health and Safety

Terotechnology for Maintenance Supervisors

Terotechnology
The Terotechnology System
Life Cycle Costs
Initial Costs
Maintenance Costs
Downtime Costs
Maintenance Management
Maintenance Planning and Control
The Computer in the Maintenance Department
Maintenance Personnel
Information and Training
Productivity and Maintenance Improvement
Maintenance Support

Costing and Budgets
Condition Monitoring
Health and Safety

Terotechnology for Procurement Officers

Terotechnology
The Terotechnology System
Life Cycle Costs
Initial Costs
Costs of Use
Downtime Costs
Purchasing
Maintainability
Quality Assurance
Delivery and Installation
Product Support and Service
Costs
Contracts
Health and Safety
The Environment
Safety of Personnel
Introduction to Computers

7

Work Planning, Productivity and Maintenance Improvement

This chapter outlines some of the planning methods used in the maintenance office and deals briefly with various aspects of work measurement. Finally other ways of improving maintenance performance are discussed.

Job Analysis

Work planning in the maintenance department begins with job analysis – the process of identifying the major tasks in any particular work programme and in establishing a breakdown of these into minor tasks so that ideal work sequences can be developed. A simple example is seen in motor vehicle servicing as shown in Figure 7:1.

Examination of Figure 7:1 indicates how the jobs are related and how jobs requiring the same preliminary stages and the same following stages can be performed at the same time to advantage. This simple example indicates the uses of job analysis in planning work sequences. In this case tasks A6 and A8 might be combined to prevent unnecessary repetition of preliminary stages A1 and A5.

A further stage of job analysis can be undertaken to indicate in detail the estimated times to completion, also the tools, spares and material requirements.

From Figure 7:2 a schedule of total time taken, manpower requirements and tools needed can be established. This type of schedule of routine work provides the basis for work sequence planning, manpower estimates, etc. on estimated times with the possibility of formal work study being introduced at a later date if required. Applied to routine overhaul work (pumps, motors, etc.) the schedule can be developed to provide the basis for benchmark standard times.

Bar Charts

A major task consisting of a number of minor tasks of varying sizes can be portrayed on a bar chart divided vertically in days or weeks (Figure 7:3). Estimated times for the various minor tasks are shown as blocks on the chart, each block being displaced horizontally to its earliest possible starting date. Tasks which are interdependent are arranged on the same horizontal line, the critical path being that line which establishes the earliest possible finishing date for the entire project. Where a task has an earliest starting date and a latest finishing date defining a period which exceeds the required time for the task, a slack period is said to exist. For example, task 3 which is executed within task 2 has a slack period of one week.

Codes may also be added to the blocks to indicate the number and grades of labour required. A vertical summation is then possible to determine the maximum numbers of tradesmen required. Horizontal movement of the tasks is then possible, within the slack periods, to reduce peak labour requirements as far as possible. The bar chart can be drawn on a standardized blank sheet or produced on a planning board using magnetic or other display techniques. For annual shutdown maintenance, or for major plant overhauls, the bar chart provides a convenient method of presenting critical paths, slack periods and peak labour requirements.

Critical Path Networks

Planning within the maintenance department should aim to develop a situation in which the operation of an annual or other periodic programme of work can be set in motion, and controlled effectively through a work plan which, although perhaps produced for a specific occasion, can be referred to whenever an identical task, or a task containing similar elements, is expected. This can greatly simplify the approach to annual shutdown work, to plant overhaul between seasons of high production or to the summer maintenance programme on domestic systems. With this type of plan in reserve, the chief engineer can order extensive work with full manpower, tools and spares resourcing by calling for 'Plan 2, E factory, commencing June 16' without extensive use of planning unless, of course, detailed changes are required by changed circumstances (Figure 7:4).

Many forms of planning are used, many of them based upon the critical path network; one form of which is illustrated and explained here. In this example the square indicates an event, a point in time indicating the beginning or end of a task, and the arrow portrays an activity, the work necessary to produce the event. In this case all the events shown are beginnings: for example, commence overhaul of No. 2 conveyor. The network begins with a single event (remove covers from X freezer tunnel) and expands into a number of activities which link events in the total plan. The network ends with a single event ('carry out test procedure RS4/2' is an example) and the chain of events producing the longest time from the beginning event to the final event determines the minimum length of time required to execute the plan and is therefore the 'critical path'. Networks may be constructed in a 'forward' direction, from beginning event to final event or in a 'backward' direction, beginning with the concluding event. If the time available for the project exceeds the total time of the critical path on the plan there is said to be positive slack time. Negative slack occurs when the critical path indicates that the permitted shutdown period is inadequate for the work programme as defined by the network plan.

The first task for the planner is the preparation of a total activity list for the project with estimated times for each activity. It will probably be necessary to divide the activities in terms of trade skills, although this can be done later when the programme is developed and manpower resourcing is attempted. A typical activity list might include:

Activity number	Activity details	Labour	
		Men	Days
1	Remove covers, clean down	1 Fitter	1
		3 Labourers	1
2	Disconnect electric motors (12)	1 Electrician	0.6
3	Remove motors, remove gearboxes, deliver motors to goods dispatch department	2 Fitters	1.5
		2 Mates	1.5
4	Overhaul motors	Subcontractor	
5	Strip mixers (2)	2 Fitters	3
		2 Mates	3
		. . . Etc.	

The plan is then developed in skeleton form, each event being shown as a block on a block diagram with the interconnecting lines annotated to indicate the maximum time taken for the activity represented between events. At each stage of planning, from the preparation of the activity list, through the skeleton networks to the final agreed plan, adequate consultation with all concerned is essential. If the plan is to be accepted and adopted to the best effect a public relations job is necessary with the planning engineer establishing good relationships throughout the personnel hierarchy. Estimates for the work entailed have to be obtained by discussion with the chargehands and foremen concerned and it is at this stage that the benefits of planning are explained to encourage maximum cooperation. In broadest terms, personnel respond well to an indication that this year's overhaul will not produce the frayed tempers, frantic shopping for spares, Christmas Day working, crushed fingers and other problems remembered from previous experience. The 'PR' abilities of the planner are most important here.

When a clear picture emerges, the planning engineer should produce a draft network giving the work flow picture. This must be discussed with all concerned before further work is done. Throughout its life the plan must be regarded as a dynamic plan, capable of change to accommodate changed circumstances, with feedback to management and line supervision of any changes affecting the work programme and in particular those affecting completion dates.

The final plan portrays all the events and activities within the project and illustrates the critical path clearly. In the example, the critical path occurs through events 1, 2, 4, 9, 17, etc. which require 28, 14, 7, 28, 14, etc. days of activity. Thus activity number 2 must commence immediately after activity number 1. Slack time, as referred to earlier, also occurs between individual events but in this case, between events 1, 2, 4 etc., no slack is permitted and on the event lines a '0' (no slack) is shown. Event 3, however, which is planned to occur in parallel with event 2, requires only 7 days of activity as compared with the 14 days available. Thus, although the starting date for event 2 is fixed the date for event 3 has 7 days slack time and may occur between 28 and 35 days into the project. The network chart is a flexible tool and can be annotated numerically as shown or have actual activity titles and work programmes written in the squares or along the lines. It is useful when preparing draft networks to purchase a rubber stamp and ink pad so that the squares or other symbols used may be stamped on the drafting paper to reduce drawing time. When preparing the final version of the chart, adhesive symbols may be used to reduce drawing costs.

Work Measurement Techniques

The work measurement techniques used in the maintenance department range from simple job timing with stopwatch to the data block system MTM-2. On the one hand actual tasks are timed, wholly or partly as executed by an employee of appropriate skills level and, on the other, maintenance work is classified in terms of standard work blocks and the detailed examination of each task determines the number and type of work blocks used in any particular task. Within these extremes a number of other work measurement techniques, such as estimated time standards, are practised.

Work measurement is intended to provide a scale for the evaluation of human effort in the maintenance department. If applied without care and if used without due regard to other aspects of maintenance management and control it can adversely affect industrial relations and worsen man/management relationships. If introduced against a background of inadequate maintenance planning, ineffective stores or other supporting systems, inadequate staff training and poor technical information in the maintenance department it can result in ridicule of the management methods. If partially applied, without frequent review, as part of an incentive scheme it can produce bonus payments which eventually become a mere part of salary without true relationship to productivity. When introducing work measurement, therefore, a thorough investigation of all other management aspects is essential and care must be taken to introduce a competent and comprehensive plan.

Repetitive work in the maintenance department can be timed by normal stopwatch methods. For the most accurate results the timing operation can be repeated over a period of weeks or months to produce average results for the various personnel involved. During the measurement period, the opportunity may be taken to analyse the methods used. If the times are subdivided to show individual times for various preparatory, mainstream and closing activities, the actual work sequence may be examined and proposals made for improvement of the techniques or the order of work.

Non-repetitive work may be given a time allowance based on analytical estimating. Analytical estimating is a task for a skilled tradesman (sometimes called an applicator) who breaks down the task in terms of standard units combined with non-standard estimated work. This gives a closer control than whole-task estimating and again facilitates examination of the methods employed and the work sequences adopted. Using analytical estimating techniques results in tasks previously allocated 8 or 9 hours ('about a day' by rough estimation at supervisor level) being identified clearly as 5- or 6-hour tasks — a significant improvement in manpower resource control.

A typical task may be divided for analytical estimation in terms of:

1   Preparation (instructions, materials, tools, access equipment).
2   Travelling to site.
3   On-site preparations (safety, disconnection of power, access).
4   Removing guards.
5   Cleaning.
6   Removing covers.
7   Removing fuse holders from isolator.
8   Removing eight coupling bolts.

Where standard work data exists for a particular task, or for its near equivalent, the breakdown must isolate this task as maximum use of standard data reduces the time taken by the applicator and increases the reliability of the measured times.

Whenever analytical estimates are prepared, an immediate improvement in performance can be expected. (The inaccuracies of rough estimating are exemplified above.) However, the records show that in many maintenance departments, incentive bonuses based on estimates, formal or otherwise, have lost meaning and become part of salary. The tendency for this to happen in the maintenance department, with its considerable proportion of unplanned, emergency and diagnostic work, can be countered by frequent review of standards set, by improved management planning to reduce the proportion of unplanned work and by good industrial relations based on effective localized supervision. One function of the local supervisor (foreman, chargehand or senior tradesman) is the provision of feedback to the applicator in terms of changed methods, new techniques and possible timing variations. When the applicator prepares the initial timing for each trade employed on the task, some 10 per cent will be added for allowances. This will be removed later if possible and even greater reductions may be made as the pattern of work is established. This again requires good industrial relations and preparatory public relations activity.

In comparative estimating (originated in the USA) a catalogue of standard times (benchmarks) is developed on which time allocations may be based. The catalogue is arranged according to trade skill, type of task and time range. A time range, rather than an absolute fixed time, allows for variations in the working conditions, accessibility, equipment age and condition. Thus in the electrical class, the changing of a contactor might be allowed an average time of 0.7 hour within a real bandwidth of 0.5 to 0.9 hour.

Standard data of this type can be obtained by use of the MTM measurement system, which analyses and times basic human movements and operation stages. The operations being timed are synthetized and individual elements compared with Universal Standard Data tables to develop a total benchmark time for the complete task. For example, if the skinning of an electrical conductor is given a standard time this can be multiplied by the number of conductors to develop a total connection time for the installation of an electrical contactor. The addition of standard fixing and conduit connection data develops a total installation and wiring benchmark.

A further development is seen in the MTM-2 data block system which defines maintenance work as a series of building blocks, each block representing a handling function. The applicator can define a given task in terms of these blocks which are assembled to build the total task. The frequencies at which the individual blocks recur determine the total job time.

Use of the data block system facilitates control of the large number of maintenance tasks which fall within the minor work category — loosely classified as tasks occupying less than one man-hour. This can be 20 per cent of the total work load in a maintenance department. The applicator engaged in developing standard job times can sample these minor tasks and, using the data block principle, develop a series of average times to be applied by the local supervisors. In this way MTM-2 is applicable to maintenance tasks large or small and whether repetitive or singular in frequency.

Cost Effectiveness in Maintenance Work Measurement

Developments by the Maynard organization indicate that the time taken to time a maintenance task by MTM-2 methods can equal the actual job time multiplied by 150. The same task can be timed by use of blocks of craft data and basic operations data in only 3 to 6 times the actual job time. This latter method is illustrated by Figure 7:5 in which a time (benchmark) for the task is assembled from basic operations data (from standard MTM blocks) combined with other craft data.

The technique for measuring non-repetitive work is called Work Content Comparison. This technique produces a set of time bands and if a task is placed in the correct time band, the mid-point of the band will be sufficiently accurate as a measure for the task. The procedure is:

1   Calculate a series of time bands and display these on a 'spread sheet', see Figure 7:6.
2   Assemble benchmark times for a number of typical jobs, as shown in Figure 7:5.
3   Write a brief description of each job in the time range columns.
4   Add other jobs, which may not have occurred before and have a low repetition rate, by comparing these with the benchmark jobs and allocating to suitable time range columns.
5   Use the mid-point of the time range as the representative time.

Three work measurement techniques are commonly used for maintenance activities:

1   Direct standards — used for repetitive work, such as lubrication routines.
2   Work sheets — used for craft data calculations on painting, machining and other craft tasks.
3   Work Content Comparison — as described above — used for the majority of maintenance jobs.

Maintenance Improvement

Faced with increasing costs and a regular increase (10 per cent or more) in his annual budget, the maintenance manager must look for improved methods of working, of planning and of manpower and materials utilization. Although resistance is met when sums of money are allocated in this way, it is preferable for these requirements to be expressed upwards to the directors rather than downwards from a managing director who had identified improved methods in other, possibly competitive, installations. Many improvement projects can be tested by the maintenance manager by the transfer of money from underspent areas of the budget to provide a test case for submission when asking for further budgetary allowances. Typical maintenance improvement projects are listed below:

1   Introducing, extending or improving maintenance planning.
2   Rationalizing the investment in spares and equipment.
3   Improving stock control, spares codification and issue methods.
4   Establishing, or extending, planned overhaul of plant.
5   Introducing an overhaul-by-planned-replacement policy.
6   Producing fault diagnosis and repair charts and procedures.
7   Introducing training in fault diagnosis and other techniques.
8   Producing specialized technical manuals on vital plant.
9   Preparing job instructions or work specifications.

10   Updating plant register and reviewing job frequencies.

Although, as stated above, it is sometimes difficult to obtain budgetary provisions for improvement projects, a number of factors are influencing top management and focusing some attention upon maintenance costs and problems. Among these factors can be listed:

1   Noticeable improvements in performance in other departments in which planning, control, staff development and training have been applied.
2   The continued introduction of sophisticated and systemized equipment requiring higher maintenance skills and producing higher downtime costs.
3   The spread of multidiscipline equipment (electronic/hydraulic, computer-controlled/pneumatic, etc.) all of which produces high downtime costs with inadequate maintenance skills.
4   The economies of business management in the new multinational trading markets.
5   The costs arising from high spare parts costs, built-in obsolescence and non-repairable spares.
6   The high cost of demarcation practices when applied to maintenance of high-output, multidiscipline plant.
7   Recognition of the fact that, with a number of fixed factors (higher capital costs, higher interest charges, higher salaries, and fuel costs) in the total plant operating budget, improvement must be sought in variable factors (such as maintenance costs and administration).
8   The rising importance of maintenance and the increasing maintainer/operator ratio on modern plant installations.

It is a simple matter for management to react by introducing work measurement and productivity bargaining but, leaving aside the possible benefits or problems arising from this and looking to prevention rather than cure, attention to some of the maintenance improvement possibilities listed in the above table can produce substantial savings. So much can be achieved that work enforcement techniques may not be required or, if they are, an effective base will exist on which their application may be based.

The introduction of planning for preventive, corrective or overhaul work, where little formal organization exists, is an obvious first step in any maintenance improvement programme. When planning is practised a review may prove beneficial. This may mean updating the plant register for new or relocated items, or revision of schedules, extension of overhaul planning or a review of spares stocks, lubrication schedules, and work programmes. The rationalization of spares can also produce substantial benefits even in the extreme case where items of plant are replaced to achieve standardization. The problems arising from the use of 20 types of fork-lift truck in a fleet of 120 vehicles can be readily appreciated. Similar situations, with many different British and foreign types of equipment, develop with pumps, compressors, hydraulic items, actuators, valves and instruments, and can also benefit from recognition and investigation.

Another aspect of maintenance worthy of investigation is the fault-finding and repair performance of personnel. Improvements in fault-diagnosis and repair times produce not only direct benefits but also indirect benefits in increased productivity and reduced downtime. Reductions in diagnostic time can be achieved by the provision of diagnostic aids such as charts, manuals and detailed written procedures. These can be assisted by training programmes intended to improve understanding of the functioning of the plant with specific training in diagnostic routines. Frequently, the preparation of these charts and discussion of the practicalities of fault-finding on the plant produce a fault-finding and repair policy. This may include the addition of gauges and test points, the provision of built-in instruments for monitoring, etc. In one investigation of hydraulic control equipment, for example, charts were found to be secondary in importance; the prime requirement was for additional pressure gauges. Examination of the fault-finding and repair methods of any plant entails a degree of analysis of the engineering design and construction policies.

Other forms of documentation can be prepared to improve maintenance efficiency. These include special machine manuals for vital machines, single-discipline manuals or charts for critical electronic, hydraulic or other items which form part of a plant installation and are not fully understood by the maintainers, and detailed job instructions or work specifications for vital tasks. Not only maintenance has to be documented but also plant operation. Faulty operation can contribute noticeably to machine failure rates and downtime. A lack of understanding of the machine, its input materials and its functioning can increase wear rates and spares consumption. The development of operating instructions, also operator fault-finding charts, can reduce the frequency of calls for the maintenance man and encourage minor adjustment by the operator. A preliminary fault diagnosis by the operator can also reduce the incidence of electricians being called to mechanical faults and vice versa, also the frequency of calls for the maintenance man when in fact the input material is at fault rather than the machine.

There are many facets to the subject of maintenance improvement and maintenance managers have at times proved somewhat reluctant to advise expenditure in these ways. However the point has been made that an interest in improved methods is a natural management activity expected by directors and that suggestions should flow upwards rather than allow improvement to result only from downward pressure. As stated earlier, the case can be proved usually by a localized test financed by uncommitted budget funds or a consultant may be engaged to put a complete case for the improvement plan. Again, too few consultants are in fact called in by those who require assistance — a greater proportion being recruited by an uneasy top management.

Reference	A		B		C	
Job title	Adjust brakes		Check brake drums and shoes		Check brake mechanism	
A1	Remove wheels	A1		A1		
A2	Release handbrake	A5	Remove drums	A5		
A3	Adjust brakes	A6	Inspect drums and shoes	A8	Check brake mechanism	
A4	Replace wheels	A7	Replace drums	A7		
		A3		A3		
		A4		A4		

Figure 7:1   Task analysis sheet

Task	Schedule of work		Labour		Tools and materials
			Mechanics		
A			*No.*	*Time*	
To adjust brakes	*A1*				
	1	Remove hub cap and slacken four nuts	1	0.1	wheel brace
	2	Position jack and lift car	1	0.1	jack
	3	Remove nuts and wheel.	1	0.1	
	A2 Release handbrake				
	A3				
		Turn brake adjuster fully clockwise, turn anti-clockwise one notch. Check that wheel movement is free.	1	0.2	adjuster Ref. SK6102
	A4				
	1	Refit wheel and tighten four nuts			
	2	Lower car and remove jack	1	0.2	
	3	Tighten nuts and refit hub cap.			

Figure 7:2   Schedule of maintenance tasks

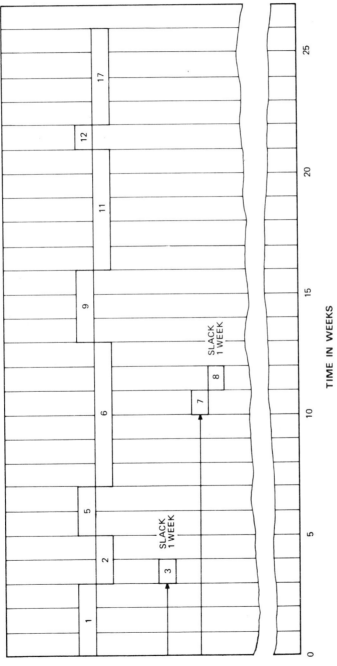

Figure 7:3   Bar chart

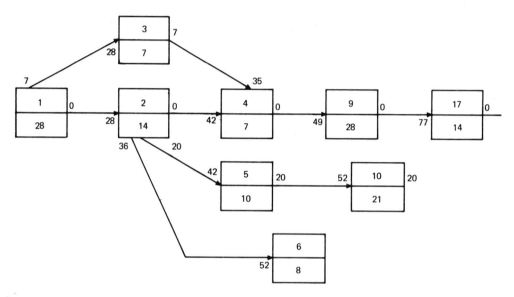

Figure 7:4   Outline diagram for critical path network

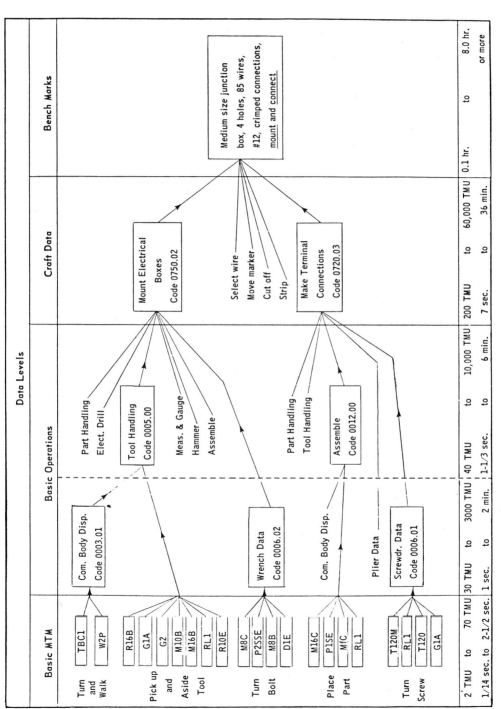

Figure 7:5   Schematic development of benchmark

Task Area: Pumps

Group D (0.7) (0.50) ... (0.90)	Group E (1.2) (0.90) ... (1.5)	Group F (2.0) (1.5) ... (2.5)	Group G (3.0) (2.5) ... (3.5)
0290-91 Rotating assembly small vertical split, disassemble and assemble	0290-195 Water well, remove and replace 1 stage (2 men)	0290-191 Pump, water well disassemble and assemble 10 foot section of discharge and oil pipe and shaft (3 men)	0290-113 Impeller, medium horizontal split pump, remove and replace from shaft (2 men)
0290-82 Rotating assembly small diagonal split, disassemble and assemble	0290-194 Water well, pull additional 10 foot section of pipe and shaft (3 men)	0290-81 Rotating assembly medium diagonal split, disassemble and assemble (2 men)	0290-193 Water well, pull 1st section of pipe and shaft (3 men)
0290-59 Rotating assembly medium vertical split, belt drive remove and replace (2 men)	0290-47 Rotating assembly small diagonal split, remove and replace	0290-94 Rotating assembly medium vertical split, disassemble and assemble	0290-87 Rotating assembly medium horizontal split, disassemble and assemble (2 men)
	0290-49 Rotating assembly small horizontal split, remove and replace	0290-60 Rotating assembly medium diagonal split remove and replace (2 men)	0290-122 Rotating assembly medium horizontal split, obstructed location, remove and replace (2 men)
	0290-57 Rotating assembly medium vertical split, coupling drive, remove and replace (2 men)	0290-62 Rotating assembly medium horizontal split, remove and replace (2 men)	0290-121 Rotating assembly medium diagonal split, obstructed location, remove and replace (2 men)
	0290-120 Rotating assembly small horizontal split, obstructed location, remove and replace	0290-119 Rotating assembly small diagonal split, obstructed location, remove and replace	

Task Area: Pumps

Figure 7:6   Example of spread sheet

8

Maintenance Support

The requirement for effective support of the maintenance men has been stated earlier and some aspects of the support organization have been suggested as subjects for maintenance improvement projects. Further information on these and other support features is given in this chapter.

Stores Organization

Most planned maintenance systems provide for effective liaison with the engineering stores which provides for their needs in terms of materials and spare parts. Many designs for simple stores requisition forms exist and sometimes provision is made for recording the stores issue on the actual work card issued to the fitters. The operation of the 'trigger' in advance of the work programme is often used to give adequate warning of impending stock withdrawals to the stores supervisor. In some sophisticated systems the necessary spares, together with work specifications, technical manuals and special tools are prepared as a complete service by the storekeeper for the execution of a particular task and are assembled in advance of the requirement arising.

The management of the stores will be organized to conform with the system selected and a number of stock control systems are available. In some installations the engineering stores is isolated from all other stores functions. However, many maintenance managers find it advantageous to limit this separation to spare parts and special tools only, obtaining cleaning materials and other consumable items from the general store. In this way, the advantages of bulk buying of standard items and services can be extended to those consumable items used within the maintenance department.

In many situations it is found convenient to have separate stores located in particular departments to provide a local service to the maintenance workers. This reduces the time taken to obtain spares and stores and provides a specialist service where particular stores requirements are originated within a section of the installation. All stores units should of course operate a stock control system, which should be frequently reviewed in the light of experience.

The procedure often used to reduce the high cost of issuing small spare parts is the 'free issue' or 'supermarket' system whereby small items such as washers, screws, cleaning cloths, grease, etc. are provided in the maintenance workshop in a series of bins or shelves which are available to all staff of the maintenance staff at all times. It is estimated that the small amount of pilfering which takes place under such a free issue system is outweighed by the high cost of issuing small items when they are issued through the normal stores procedure with its associated paperwork. It is necessary to consult the accounts department as to whether the cost of items thus stocked shall be applied to the indirect materials charge or shall be spread across a particular group of account codes. Monitoring by the accounts department will indicate whether this service is being used correctly and whether any pilfering is at an acceptable level.

Stores items and spare parts should be coded in accordance with the asset code (see Chapter 3). The importance of this is seen when examining the work patterns for the maintenance worker in a variety of situations.

1 Machine breakdown notified by operative, spare part needed.
   (*a*)   Proceed to machine, determine nature of fault, note asset number, e.g. 02–16–PU–06.
   (*b*)   Obtain spare part, item 02–16–PU–06–Z1 from row 16, bin 56 in stores.
   (*c*)   Fit spare part, complete documentation, charge work time and spare part to asset code.

2 Corrective maintenance required, work card issued, spare part required.
   (*a*)   Note asset number from work card.
   (*b*)   Obtain spare part, item 08–23–CO–01–15 from row 16, bin 56 in store.
   (*c*)   Fit spare part, complete documentation, and charge to asset code.

The essential references are the asset code and the stores bin reference. Suppliers' part numbers are only required for special purchases or restocking actions which involve the supplier. When spare parts are common items, as in the example above, the bin reference is obviously the same for two different asset part codes. A spare bearing, for example, in a particular bin in the store may be common to twenty different assets and the twenty asset part codes would all be cross-referenced to the same bin. The stores manual provides the cross references from asset code to bin number and to suppliers' number. Where possible, the components for a specific asset should be grouped in adjacent bins for fast access.

Alternative suppliers must be indicated where possible. Thus, a roller bearing may be classified as:

$$
PU-06-Z1 \left\{ \begin{array}{ll} \text{Skefco} & \text{SX 0270} \\ \text{Horstmann} & \text{H 453B} \\ \text{Ransome} & \text{214 RX3} \end{array} \right.
$$

The issue of materials and spares is made only against official requisitions issued by the planned maintenance 'trigger' system or against requisitions signed by the appropriate foremen. In a normal issue the requisition form passes after use to the stock control and records office, who amend the stock records (Figure 8:1), initiate any replacement procurements and notify the cost control office. However, when the item is not in stock the storesman, after rechecking with the foreman that the item is essential and that no other stocked item will replace it, sets the procurement activity in motion (Figure 8:2). The company procurement officer will notify the stores records office, the accounts department, the supplier and the foreman signing the request that the necessary action has been taken and also the delivery date (if predicted). When received, the item is issued in the normal way and the stores records office and accounts department notified.

When capital projects are undertaken by the maintenance department, the procurement officer is instructed by the project controller. As items are received they are stored and the stores records office and the project controller informed. When the stock is at the required level and the starting date is reached, authority for issue is given by the project control office.

Stores documentation in common use includes:

1 Stores requisition forms.
2 Daily issue sheets — completed by storesman.
3 Company order form — issued by procurement officer.
4 Advice notes — issued by suppliers.
5 Stock record cards — completed by stores record office.
6 Capital item requests — issued by project office.
7 Capital item stock lists — issued by stores record office.

When a number of stores are necessary to serve a group of buildings or a group of companies, a common approach to procurement produces useful reductions in item prices if bulk buying rates are obtained. This aspect is also improved by a policy of materials and spares rationalization as described later.

Lubricant Handling

Lubricants play an important part in machinery maintenance and must be stored and handled to minimize waste or pilfering and to prevent contamination. Liquid lubricants can be stored in bulk tanks or more flexibly in smaller tank modules, see

Figure 8:3. Zone stores or remote stores for mobile plant sites are supplied by tank modules or by oil drums. If the latter are used, barrel covers with locks are required. Dispensing equipment includes trolleys, hand pumps and measures. Mixing trolleys are available with calibrated tanks, and a variety of dispensing trolleys can be obtained for carrying oil, grease, tools and equipment for maintenance purposes.

Spares Rationalization

The increased interest shown by accountants in the investment charges and operating costs within the maintenance department has brought spare parts investments to the forefront of many cost analyses. This may lead to the use of external or internal personnel in determining whether the range of spares held relates to the likely demand, and also whether any rationalization of the spares themselves, or of the plant for which spares are held, could be beneficial. In one chemical plant, for example, it was found that the replacement of non-standard pumps, accompanied by the resale of the unwanted pumps and spares, would produce significant reductions in spares stocks and in maintenance costs, and would facilitate an 'overhaul-by-exchange' programme reducing the need for shutdowns during pump maintenance.

A review of a maintenance store which has developed over a period of years often indicates:

1   Considerable applications for rationalization.
2   Redundant spares — often of high value to other plant users.
3   Spare parts which in themselves require maintenance and repair.
4   Problems of spare parts identification, particularly for spares long held.
5   Possible economies in operation and methods.

However, inflation has also affected the cost of spare parts and this is particularly true for spares for imported machinery. Spare parts can be a good investment if they are for current assets and have strategic value. If this can be proved by the maintenance manager, any attempts by the finance department to enforce reductions in spares holdings can often be resisted.

Particular attention to the rationalization aspects are necessary when procuring new plant or equipment. Pumps, valves, actuators, motors, transistors, relays, controls tend to vary widely throughout an installation particularly when large parts of a complex job are subcontracted to various plant vendors each having their own preferences for suppliers of components. Thus a process plant having four distinct stages, each let to a major subcontractor, may have four or more suppliers of pneumatic actuators or electrically operated valves spread over two or three countries. Not only does this increase the investment in spare parts but it complicates the training and familiarization of maintenance staff, increases maintenance costs and inhibits component interchange in emergency.

Vendor Assistance

With the influx of sophisticated control equipment, the buyer may wish to include vendor assistance clauses in procurement contracts. These may require vendor participation in installation, commissioning, spare parts provisioning, and standby or contract maintenance services during the first six months or two years of operation. Vendor assistance in the domestic equipment field (air conditioning, heating, refrigeration, etc.) is less common, with a higher proportion of the work passing to the growing contract service companies.

Although vendor assistance may be essential when, for example, a process is first computerized and new maintenance skills are urgently required, most maintenance managers prefer to regard this as a short term measure. Among the problems encountered with continued vendor assistance are:

1   The cost – particularly when vendors second their development engineers to emergency work.
2   The delay – even one hour may be very costly on high-output plant.
3   The possibility of unrecorded modifications to the plant by vendor engineers.
4   The failure to develop expertise amongst the maintenance department personnel.
5   Possible high spares costs where parts bought by the vendor from other suppliers carry his extra costs.
6   Inadequate disclosure of technical information by the vendor to in-plant personnel.

The continued involvement of vendor engineers can make the maintenance manager permanently dependent upon the vendor's service operation if retained expertise by vendor engineers causes a shortage of information and a lack of training within the maintenance department. The offer of vendor service, a profitable venture for many plant suppliers, can further hinder the development of effective product support techniques (described elsewhere in this book) at a period when plant and equipment is more complex than ever before, requiring maximum formal disclosure of operating and maintenance information by the vendors.

One aspect of vendor assistance which can be cost saving relates to spare parts stocks. The buyer may negotiate with the vendor an arrangement by which a stock of major spares items is maintained at the vendor's premises. In this way, buyers of the plant or equipment have a reduced investment in spare parts whilst the vendor can service the spares needs of a number of users from a limited spares stock. However, the buyer entering into such a contract must determine the purchase price of the items, if consumed during the period of the contract, and should ensure that the items referred to are in fact of the vendor's own manufacture and not 'bought-in' components subject to additional charges, overheads, etc.

When buying new plant and equipment the buyer should attempt some level of analysis of vendor assistance costs. To do this it is necessary to ask for itemized quotations for installation, commissioning, technical assistance and product support costs. An inclusive price for both plant and vendor assistance provides no basis for cost comparisons. The analysis might disclose the comparative costs for:

1   Purchasing the product support package only and making separate arrangements for staff training, commissioning and maintenance.
2   Providing maintenance department staff for training in the vendor's factory. This staff then to install and commission the plant.
3   Allowing the vendor to install, commission and service the plant.

Contract Servicing.

Contract personnel may be used within the maintenance department either to perform specific tasks on a repetitive or single contract basis or to provide additional labour at peak periods of work. Typical uses in these categories are:

Specific tasks (single contract)
1   Commission new plant.
2   Carry out a specific overhaul programme.
3   Prepare or update plant register.
4   Review spares stock.
5   Prepare maintenance schedules.

Specific tasks (repetitive)
1   Carry out preventive maintenance routines.
2   Prepare plant for statutory inspection.
3   Operate vehicles maintenance system.
4   Provide 'on-call' emergency maintenance.

Labour only contracts
1   Provide additional manpower during overhaul programme.
2   Supply maintenance labour during holiday periods.
3   Assist with planning work.
4   Update or review maintenance schedules.

Increasing use of service contracts for the maintenance of both services plant and process machinery is reflected in the growth of the service companies in the 1970s. In domestic maintenance situations (hospitals, local authority buildings, offices and other properties) the total service concept embracing both preventive and emergency maintenance is accepted practice.

The range of services offered by service contracts (Figures 8:4 and 8:5) include:

1   Full planned preventive maintenance, inclusive or exclusive of materials and

spares.

2 Full planned preventive maintenance, plus emergency service.

3 Full planned preventive maintenance with an emergency service on an 'at-cost' basis.

4 Emergency 'on-call' service only.

5 Preventive maintenance only.

When employing a contract service organization the buyer must look for:

1 An organization large enough to guarantee adequate technical resources and effective coverage of the district in which the asset is located.

2 A personalized service with named contact men to provide direct links between the companies.

3 The organization must indicate its ability to tailor a system to meet the user's requirements.

4 Stability in the contractor's work force so that acquired knowledge of the equipment and its location remains at the buyer's disposal.

5 An effective control system so that work carried out can be related to accounts rendered.

6 Good labour relations policies, incentives, supervision, bonuses, staff attitudes.

7 Effective control over variable factors such as extra work, materials used, spares consumed, etc.

8 A list of satisfied users to whom reference may be made. In this respect, confirmation that the above points are attended to will be more significant than experience in a particular application.

Product Support

The preferred definition of product support is given below. However, the definition indicates two distinct sectors: 'product support' and 'customer service' which are combined in many companies and non-existent in some vendor companies.

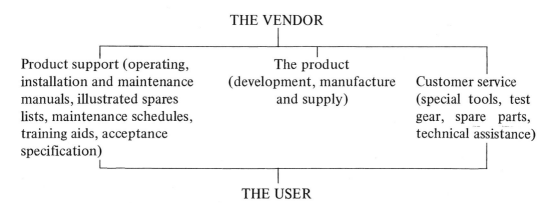

The most effective product support and customer service operations are seen in those companies which rent and service equipment (office equipment, computers, etc.). The cost of poor product support by such companies would reflect directly upon their maintenance costs and, therefore, upon their profitability. Much can be learned from these companies and from the armed services, where product support contributes to the total defence capability. Such equipment is designed for fast fault diagnosis, for easy access to components or replacement modules and for reliability in operation. Product support documentation is produced during the development and manufacture of the plant and reflects the maintenance policies adopted. Feedback from the product support personnel and the customer service department assists the designer in providing low-cost maintenance features.

In the simplest case a product support package might consist of a small booklet containing operating and minor maintenance procedures with an illustrated list of spare parts. (This would be adequate for a portable tool or a manually operated machine.) For a more complex machine or group of machines a separate operating, cleaning and minor adjustments manual would be required together with full maintenance manuals, a training programme and illustrated spares books. For a systemized machine or plant it is important that the product support package provides operating, fault-finding and maintenance information at system level followed by information expressed in descending orders to the level of the lowest replaceable item.

A product support system

A comprehensive product support system, as required for a process plant, transport installation, or other complex of plant and machinery would consist of the following items:

Item	Name	Function
A	Technical specifications	To define the parameters and technical features of the plant. To define the various types or models available.
B	Operator instruction cards	To provide convenient operating instructions for use with the product. On small appliances these replace item C. Both items B and C are provided for more sophisticated products.
C	Operating manuals	To enable the product to be installed and commissioned. To provide operating instructions including operator maintenance and fault diagnosis (if permitted) also safety procedures and instructions for obtaining technical assistance.
D	Maintenance manuals	To provide complete technical descriptions, fault-diagnosis, repair and overhaul, and routine maintenance procedures.

Item	Name	Function
E	Maintenance instruction cards	To be used by engineers working on the product. On small appliances these replace item D. Both items D and E are supplied for sophisticated products. Maintenance instruction cards can also form part of a scheduled servicing system – see item N.
F	Containers	To contain technical documentation, particularly in a maintenance department environment.
G	Spare parts lists	These must be fully illustrated. On small appliances these may be included in items C or D.
H	Wall diagrams	To be displayed in workshops and to be used during training of personnel.
J	Films (if necessary)	To be used for training.
K	Transparencies	To be used for training. Transparencies and microforms are now used in portable viewing machines or projectors during maintenance.
L	Training manuals	To be used for training. If a qualified instructor is available, item C can be used as a training manual. Training manuals are often written in programmed format. Individual engineers may operate a self-teach project using items H, K and L.
M	Plant register cards	To provide a basis for planned maintenance or scheduled servicing. When supplied with industrial plant, these items become part of the planned maintenance system.
N	Work instruction cards	
O	Cost cards	
P	Work specifications	
R	Work schedules.	

Although the word 'manual' has been used when referring to printed technical information this does not necessarily imply a presentation in book form. Other methods of presentation are described later in this chapter. The design of the package and the method of presentation may be varied according to the requirements of the user and, if necessary, a consultant employed by the user or, at the user's request, by the vendor to ensure that the best result is obtained.

The production of product support material is sometimes left to the design engineers, who not only produce design oriented information but also are not available to even start the work until the plant has been commissioned. Thus the information may be both late and unsuitable, and also expensive to prepare. Sometimes other vendor staff (draughtsmen, technical writers, etc.) are used in this work and on occasions this also produces information which is text oriented and is descriptive with insufficient attention to fault-finding, repair and scheduled maintenance. Where there is doubt as to the quality, comprehensiveness or suitability of the completed product support system the user must employ a consultant or provide the means for specialist help to the vendor during plant development and manufacture.

Technical Manuals (Reference 4)

The technical manual is a most important product support item and is usually produced first, as many extracts from it are suitable for use in the development of training aids, fault diagnosis and maintenance procedures. When newly developed products or systems are supplied it is common practice to provide a provisional manual, the final version being prepared after commissioning. As mentioned earlier, the maintenance manual may not in fact be a book but may take the form of work cards, wall diagrams, a microfilm, or any combination of these forms of presentation. Some special types of maintenance oriented information are listed in Figure 8:6. The following specification for technical information required on a project may be applied to any form of presentation.

To meet its objectives the manual must provide a permanent record of the technical information required to understand, operate and maintain the plant and to train operatives and maintenance workers. The information requirements of the user may be identified and satisfied as follows:

Information required	Section of manual
What is the plant and what is it for?	1 Technical data (specification)
How do we use it?	2 Operating information
How does it work?	3 Technical description
How do we handle it?	4 Handling instructions
How do we maintain it?	5 Maintenance instructions
How do we care for it?	6 Maintenance schedules
What does it consist of?	7 Spare parts lists
Details of variations and improvements	8 Modifications

Section contents

The contents of these sections should include the following information:—

1 *Technical data*
   (a) Statistics, dimensions, weights, supply requirements, environmental factors, performance data, manning, etc.
   (b) List of data (specifications, reports, drawings, etc.).
   (c) Hazard warnings and precautions in connection with use of the plant.
2 *Operating information*
   (a) Description of operating modes.
   (b) Operating procedures (normal and emergency) with safety notes.
   (c) Operator fault diagnosis, also maintenance and adjustment procedures (if permitted).
   (d) Procedures for monitoring and reporting failures.

3   *Technical description*
    (*a*)   Full technical details of system or machine.
    (*b*)   Full technical description of functional parts of system or machine.
    (*c*)   Full technical description of supporting plant (power sources, test gear, etc.).
4   *Handling instructions*
    (*a*)   Handling, transportation and unpacking.
    (*b*)   Installation and connection details.
    (*c*)   Commissioning and proving procedures.
    (*d*)   Relocation, storage or disposal instructions.
5   *Maintenance instructions*
    (*a*)   Fault diagnosis routines and performance checks.
    (*b*)   Minor maintenance tasks (calibration, adjustments, minor repairs, etc.).
    (*c*)   Repair instructions (dismantling, repair or overhaul, reassembly and testing).
6   *Maintenance schedules*
    (*a*)   Preventive maintenance procedures.
    (*b*)   Calibration, overhaul and repair schedules.
7   *Spare parts lists*
    (*a*)   System or machine identification drawings.
    (*b*)   Illustrated parts lists.
    (*c*)   Illustrated tool and test gear lists.
8   *Modifications*
    (*a*)   Vendor modifications information.
    (*b*)   User modifications instructions.

A specification for the preparation of these sections appears as Appendix 2 to this book.

Simplified Technical Instructions

A most important step in providing simplified technical information has been the development by the Caterpillar Tractor Company of their 'Fundamental English' system, now available in all languages as the International Language for Servicing and Maintenance (Reference 5). This system controls the variety of words used in technical information, ensures simplified and standardized grammatical constructions, and eliminates synonyms, ensuring that each word has one clear meaning. Caterpillar produce technical manuals and training programmes for their products using less than 800 different words, plus part names. ILSAM can be used in any national language and provides clear, direct and unambiguous instructions.

Language barriers are crossed quite easily in one of two ways. Firstly, foreign users can be taught the shortened vocabulary in English so that within a few days they can use instructions in the original language. Secondly, if translations are preferred they can be prepared easily and quickly from the standardized text. The translator, or even a computer, changes the standard words from the source language to equivalent words in the target language. Manual editing is then necessary to ensure readability. Communication between technical personnel of different races, or between personnel of the same race but different educational levels, is possible with full comprehension and a common understanding of every word.

Machine Manuals

Most maintenance managers are responsible for some plant or equipment which has been supplied with inadequate documentation. In many cases this has been obtained from foreign sources but the problem can occur even when the design is by an in-plant department. The proportion of total plant in this category may vary from 30 to 70 per cent, of which only 25 to 50 per cent contributes significantly to downtime. Where this is seen to constitute a problem, machine manuals can be prepared retrospectively by consulting engineers and technical illustrators working from direct contact with the plant. The techniques used are mainly graphical as follows:

Information	*Presentation*
Operating instructions	Step-by-step procedures based on drawings
Calibration and adjustment	Step-by-step procedures based on drawings
Fault diagnosis	Algorithms, flow charts, dependency charts
Major repair/overhaul	Step-by-step procedures based on 'exploded' drawings
Lubrication schedules, cleaning procedures, safety precautions, etc.	Step-by-step procedures based on 'exploded' drawings (when required)

The machine manual provides a permanent record in a graphical easily-retrieved format. It standardizes practices between shift workers and reduces maladjustment and mis-operation problems. Fault diagnosis is speeded and unproductive downtime reduced.

Work Specifications

Whenever possible the contents of the maintenance manual should include instructions prepared in work specification format. Where these are not included work specifications may be specially prepared by maintenance department staff or contract planning personnel. Specifications may be prepared for preventive, corrective, emergency or scheduled overhaul work, each being complete in itself without cross reference to other documents. Frequently a suitable drawing is prepared and the instructions added to it. This may then form a job instruction card for workshop use if suitably protected with adhesive plastic film or a plastic bag.

Work specifications must be clear and unambiguous. A numerical sequence must be followed and all part names used be identical with those in the parts list. Instructions must be concise and terse with no unnecessary articles or conjunctions. A typical example is given in Figure 8:9.

Spare-Parts Lists

The exploded perspective drawing commonly used for illustrated spare-parts lists in vendor manuals (Figure 8:10) is of enormous importance as a technical information source in the maintenance department. So much so that plant provided without these drawings cannot really be regarded as wholly maintainable. The drawings are used as a guide to dismantling and reassembly as well as for parts identification and are frequently used as wall charts or as part of work specifications or job instructions.

Thus all spare-parts lists should be illustrated in this way, the parts being numerically annotated at the edges of the drawing. Numerical annotation, with a separate parts list, is also convenient when translations of the part names have to be made. When the lists are presented in book form the list should face its illustration. When an assembly from a large machine is illustrated in this way it is useful to add a small sketch identifying the position of the assembly within the whole machine.

The list should contain the following information:

Figure number
Item number } These key the part to the illustrated item.

Vendor's part name − This should be the exact name used on vendor drawings, in the manuals and in the vendor's service department.

Vendor's part number − For spares requests.

Number required − When more than one of the items is necessary to complete the assembly (e.g. Washers (8)).

Supplier's name
Supplier's reference
number } Where items are 'bought-in' by the plant vendor, the user may require to purchase on a direct basis for reasons of location, speed or economy.

Note: The recommended stock levels may be included but are subject to variation and may therefore be presented on a separate page or pages.

Fault Diagnosis Charts

In a particular fault situation on an item of plant 40 to 80 per cent of the out-of-service time or downtime may result from diagnosis of the fault condition and identification of the faulty component. A considerable reduction in this part of the total downtime is possible by the introduction of logical fault-finding techniques. These are frequently based upon flow charts prepared in advance and issued as manuals, cards, wall charts or even microfilms or transparencies. Two well-known examples of these charts are the algorithm and the dependency chart (Figure 8:11).

The algorithm uses three basic symbols although variations and additions may be made as required. The sequence providing the most logical approach to a fault condition is illustrated by use of these symbols in a logical tree. The engineer is directed by a series of yes/no, go/no-go situations linked by observations or actions along a particular route from start to conclusion. The diagnostic path is firmly defined and the correct sequence must be followed, this leading to some objections to the method by qualified engineers.

The extent to which algorithms can be used in a given situation is linked with the number and the size of drawings needed to cover the system fully. In some uses it is convenient to use algorithms to a certain level and then revert to the use of other drawings or diagrams such as the dependency chart. This also reduces objections to the de-skilling effect of the algorithmic method.

The second method of preparing fault diagnosis information is the dependency chart which uses only three basic symbols to present in chart form the functional sequences within a machine or system and to outline the dependencies between the various inputs, outputs and functional elements. Again, variations are possible and other symbols may be added.

All test points and all inputs and outputs are indicated on the chart and signal specifications given to define the ideal values expected at each point. The maintenance dependency chart has universal application for all engineering disciplines.

The maintenance dependency chart enables the 'half-split' method of fault-diagnosis to be applied, thus reducing the total diagnostic time (Figure 8:12). A test point near the centre of the chart is selected for the first test and this immediately determines which half of the system contains the fault, thus halving the number of tests to be made. A similar 'splitting' action continues until the faulty element (amplifier, relay contact, switch, valve, etc.) is located.

Again the dependency chart encourages a logical approach to fault-finding and reduces the downtime significantly. However, the dependency chart does permit the engineer to choose his own route through the system, using his knowledge of the dependency structure as shown on the chart.

Each of these methods produces information which can be produced in card form for display in the workshop or to be carried by the engineer. Reference to large and complex drawings is avoided and the logical approach, diagnosis based on the dependency structure, is cultivated.

System Documentation

The technical information required for maintenance of a system (as distinct from an item of plant or equipment) is required to be presented in a series of levels ranging from the highest or system level down to the lowest or component level. In this context a component is the smallest item replaced under the repair policy adopted which in an electronic system, for example, may vary from an individual transistor to a complete replaceable module containing 20 transistors. On a fork lift truck the starter motor may be replaced as a complete item or may be repaired down to bearing or carbon brush level. These policies must be reflected in the documentation provided.

At system level the plant is described by a functional block diagram which shows clearly the relationships between the various major sub-divisions of the system whether these divisions are in functional or physical terms. Each block on the system diagram is the subject of a further block diagram at the next level and so on until the lowest level is reached. A dependency chart may be drawn for each block diagram, each functional element on the chart corresponding to a block on the diagram.

Using functional block diagrams and dependency charts a system may be presented for technical appreciation and fault diagnosis at all levels. Once an understanding of the functions is achieved and the approach to fault-finding developed, recourse to conventional manuals and spare parts lists may be made for detailed information. Functional block diagrams and dependency charts are features of FIMS and SIMM, new technical information systems used by British and American armed forces, where significant reductions in diagnostic times and training times for maintenance personnel have been recorded.

Product Support for Buildings

Technical information is essential for buildings and for buildings services installations. Some or all of the following items will be required by the maintenance department.

Buildings
    Building manual
    Manuals of supplier's literature
    Item and materials schedules
    As-installed drawings
    Maintenance log book
    Maintenance planning charts
    Design drawing and specifications.

Building Services Installations
   Technical specifications
   Assets register
   Technical manuals
   Manuals of supplier's literature
   Equipment schedules
   As-installed drawings
   System diagrams
   Schedules of recommended spares
   Maintenance log book
   Maintenance planning charts

The guidelines for the preparation of plant manuals, given earlier in this chapter, apply to technical manuals for building services installations.

Microfilmed Data

Studies have shown that engineers devote considerable time to the retrieval of technical information. Rising labour costs have focused attention on methods of reducing this time and the magnitude of the problem is increased if downtime occurs on high-output plant. Elsewhere in this report the importance of (a) providing sufficient information and (b) structuring the data for fast retrieval is emphasized; this section refers to a further sophistication – the use of microfilmed presentation.

Early users of microfilm for maintenance data were airline maintenance departments who developed two applications:

1   Cassetted technical manuals information for servicing.
2   Microfilmed information for overhaul and repair workshops.

In the servicing application, 2,500 technical manual pages are contained in one cassette. Amendment action is inexpensive and rapid. In the workshop where overhaul work is done, dismantling and repair data is displayed and 'exploded' illustrations shown for parts identification. When producing microfilms it is not sufficient to merely film the pages of a technical document in sequence. Some editing and structuring of the information is necessary if retrieval times are to be minimized.

Another use for microfilming is in connection with detailed drawings for plant and buildings. In modern office blocks, for example, microfilmed drawings are retained in the engineering control office and are projected for examination on wall or screen during engineering briefing meetings. When installations are modified it is useful to retain microfilms of both new and old drawings, so that essential services hidden by decor or other changes can be located. The feasibility study on information recording and presentation for a new project should include investigation of microfilm techniques, especially now that some plant contractors use, and can supply, microfilmed drawings.

Drawing Libraries

It is essential when procuring plant and equipment to specify and enforce the supply of technical drawings detailing the installation, assembly, piping and wiring. This gives rise to a requirement for a drawing library which may be centralized or may be divided to provide on-site technical information in individual buildings or plant lines. Drawing files in common use range from plan chests, in which drawings are filed horizontally, to a wide variety of vertical suspension cabinets.

When drawings are required on site they may be sealed in plastic film and suspended on trolley carriers or hinged wall-mounted carriers which open to permit inspection of the drawings (Figure 8:13). In general, most drawings benefit from photographic reduction in that they are easier to use under working conditions providing that the wording and numbers remain one-sixteenth of an inch in height or approximately an 8-point type size.

If drawings are to be stored on microfilm the standard 35 mm system may be used with the films mounted on aperture cards. These are easily retrieved from file for reprinting in larger sizes or for projection and viewing. Portable viewing devices are also available, or viewing monitors may be located at suitable points in the working area or in each building of an industrial site. As mentioned above, lettering sizes must be maintained if projections or reprints are to be legible. The standard of lettering is also important. Stencilled letters and numerals are best but hand printing is acceptable if the quality is good.

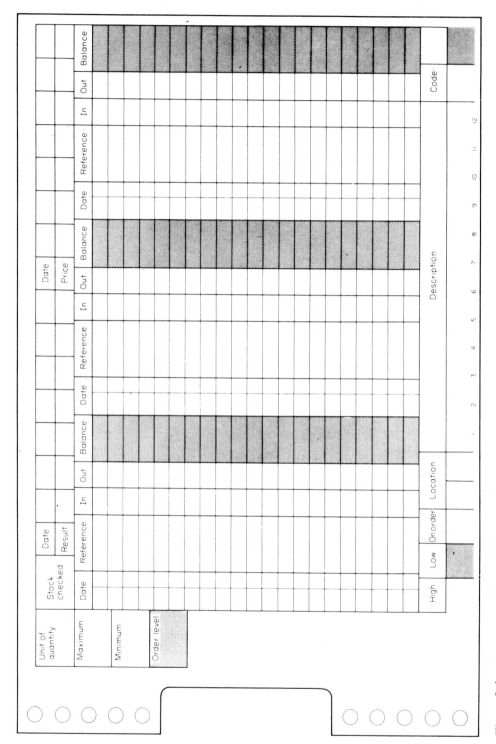

Figure 8:1 Stores record form (Kalamazoo)

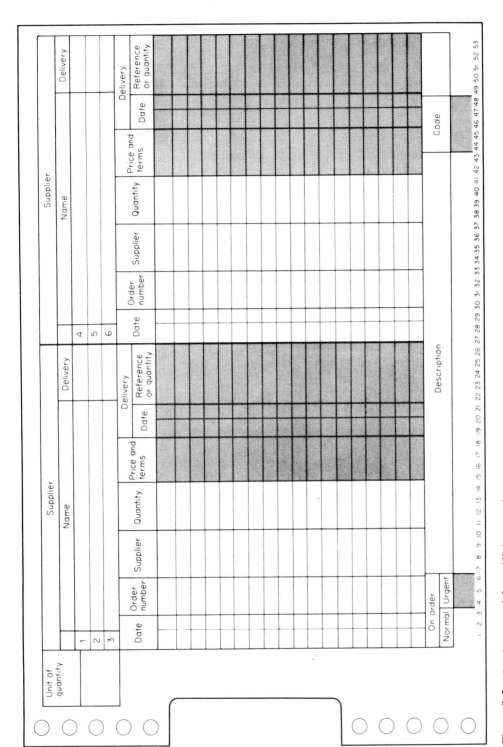

Figure 8:2 Buying record form (Kalamazoo)

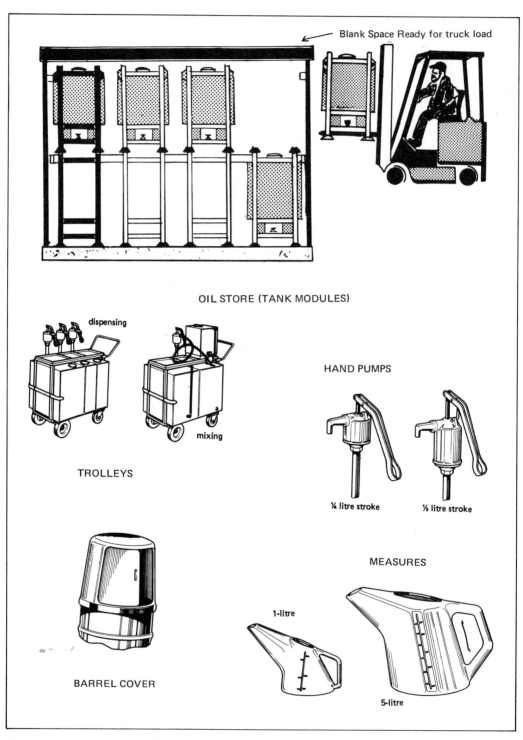

Blank Space Ready for truck load

OIL STORE (TANK MODULES)

dispensing

mixing

TROLLEYS

HAND PUMPS

¼ litre stroke

½ litre stroke

BARREL COVER

MEASURES

1-litre

5-litre

Figure 8:3   Lubricant handling

SERVICE ENGINEERS REPORT

SS SEAFLAME

Nº 343   DEER PARK ROAD MORDEN LONDON SW19 3UF   TELEPHONE 01-540 0341   Nº 343

447 _____   447 _____

SITE _____   SERVICE CARRIED OUT   DATE _____
     _____   1. MAJOR-ITEMS _____
     _____   2. MINOR-ITEMS _____   FITTER/S _____

Item No	EQUIPMENT	No Off	LOCATION	PAYMENT CODE	Engineers Signature
1					
2					
3					
4					
5					
6					
7					
8					
9					
10					
			Total Travel Hours Payable		Payment Sign.

THE ITEMS ABOVE HAVE BEEN SERVICED TO MY   CLIENT
SATISFACTION AND ARE IN GOOD WORKING ORDER   SIGNATURE _____

ENGINEERS REPORT (If separate detailed Report required tick here ☐)

Variation Order Number   (If any)

INVOICE DETAILS	£	p.
1) ROUTINE VISIT PAID IN ADVANCE		
2) ROUTINE VISIT MAJOR/MINOR CHARGEABLE		
3) CHARGE FOR MATERIAL FITTED @ _____ % ON COST		
4) TIME AND MATERIAL ORDER _____ HOURS @ _____ PER HOUR		
TOTAL		

SEAFLAME COMPANY LTD—A BOC—CAMERON COMPANY

Figure 8:4   Contract engineers report form

VARIATION ORDER/CALL OUT RECORD

SEAFLAME

Nº   0505

447

DEER PARK ROAD MORDEN LONDON SW19 3UF   TELEPHONE 01-540 0341

447 Nº   0505

SITE _____

_____

_____

Time Received _____

Time on _____

Time off _____

Date _____

Engineer _____

Total Hours _____

VARIATION ORDER — CLIENT'S ORDER NO _____

Please carry out the following work to be charged at
agreed rates in annual maintenance contract

Client Signature_____

Material Required/Fitted   Seaflame Order Placed M _____

Client Signature
for satisfactory
completion

Fitter Sign _____

Work Complete

PES Sign for
Payment

CALL OUT

Fault

Action Taken

(Materials to Complete Above)

Client Signature
for Satisfactory
completion

Fitter Signature

PES Sign for
Payment

INVOICE DETAILS

1) _____ HRS @ _____ PER HOUR

2) _____ COST MATERIAL PLUS _____ %

£   p

SEAFLAME COMPANY LTD —A BOC—CAMERON COMPANY

Figure 8:5   Variation order/call out record
Used by engineers to record extra work or emergency work and to obtain customer
authorization.

Title	Presentation	Usage
1. Machine manual (adjustment, calibration and fault-finding information presented graphically)	Few pages of plastic or oil-resistant paper (Figure 8:7)	Packaging machines or other high-speed plant. Informs maintenance men, standardizes calibration and adjustment of machines especially on shift working
2. One-sheet manual (contents as for item 1)	Flexible plastic sheet or wall-mounted card	As above. Useful in hot, dirty or otherwise difficult plant conditions
3. Mini-manuals (two small manuals in plastic cover)	Flip-over, palm-sized books, plastic cover	One book for 'installation and operation', the other for 'maintenance and repair'. Suitable for single-handed use. Ideal for instrumentation and small machines
4. Four-page manuals	Printed on plastic or oil-resistant paper	Ideal for small electrical or electronic equipment. Graphical information reduces size and weight
5. FIMS manual (a British Defence Department development)	Few pages	Suitable for electrical or electronic or other system installations. Information starts with system block diagram and is developed diagrammatically through various levels in accordance with maintenance policy
6. Integrated information system	Plasticized cards in container positioned near plant (Figure 8:8)	Cards may be colour-coded for various functions (operating, fault diagnosis, preventive maintenance, etc.). Block diagram shows functional layout of plant and gives fault-finding procedure for plant services

Figure 8:6   Special types of maintenance oriented documentation

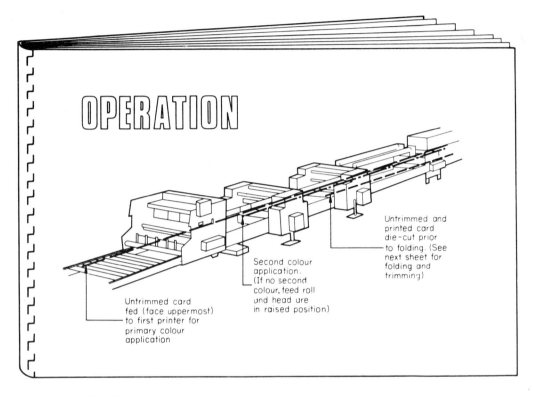

Figure 8:7   Machine manual

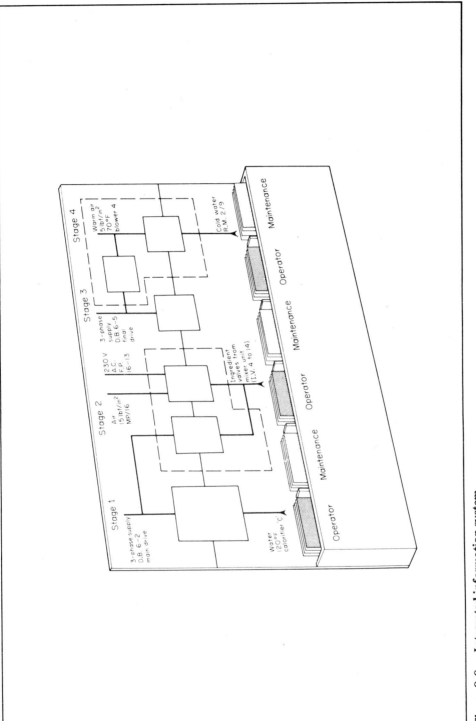

Figure 8:8   Integrated information system

Plant item	Fuel oil pump
	To overhaul pump —
1	Remove coupling guard. Remove coupling bolts.
2	Remove motor fixing bolts and remove motor.
3	Remove pump half coupling and key.
4	Clean shaft and key to remove burrs.
5	Disconnect and remove seal pipe.
6	Remove screws and withdraw seal housing and 'O' ring.
7	Slacken grubscrews and withdraw seal rotating assembly. Discard 'O' seal ring. Clean shaft.
8	Remove setscrews and withdraw suction end cover complete with rotor bush and thrust pad.
9	Remove and store spring dowel.
	Note: Idler rotors are in two halves. Lift suction end half clear as it emerges from the sleeve.
10	Wash and examine all components for wear or damage.

Figure 8:9   Work specification

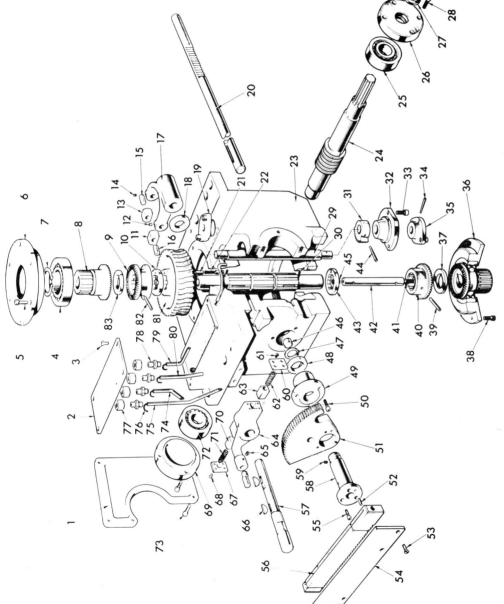

Figure 8:10   Exploded perspective drawing

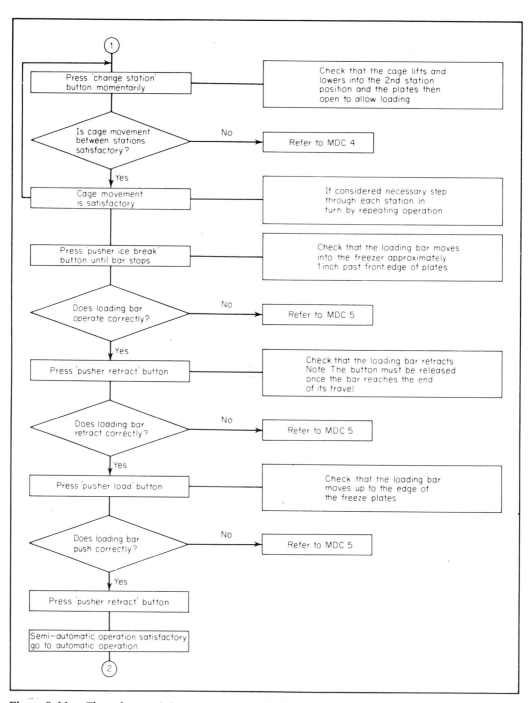

Figure 8:11   Flow chart and dependency chart (MDC)

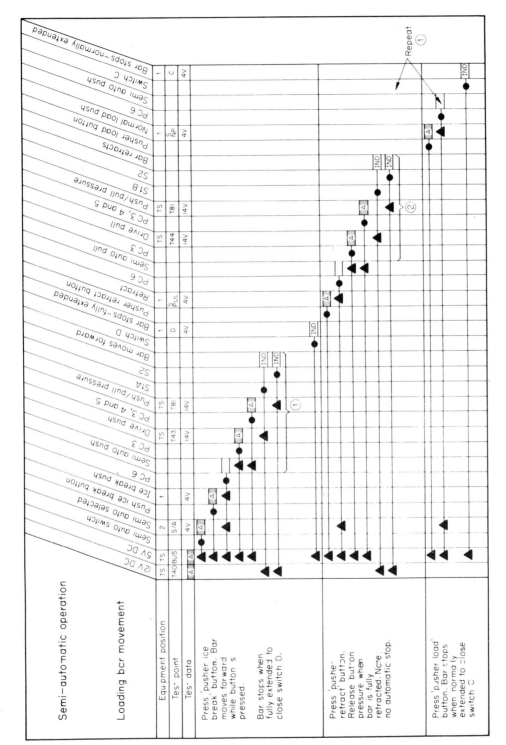

Figure 8:11 — continued

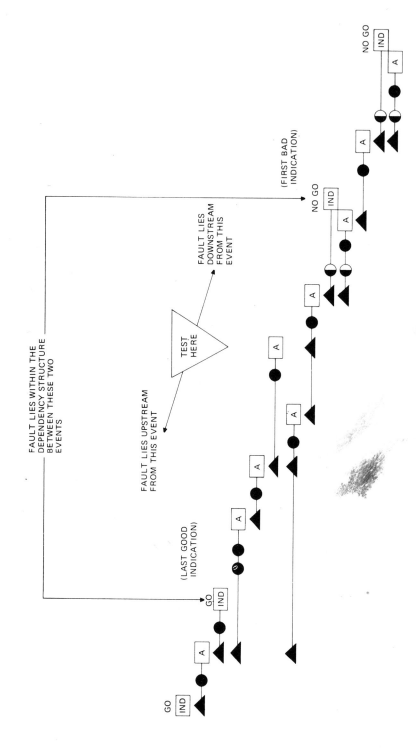

Figure 8:12   Half-split method of fault diagnosis using dependency chart

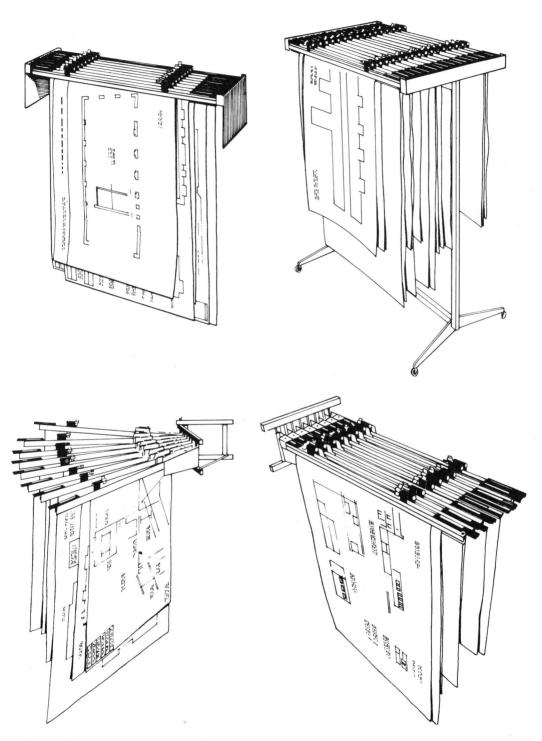

Figure 8:13   Suspension systems for engineering drawings

9

Condition-based
Maintenance

Introduction

The definition of condition-based maintenance is 'Maintenance work initiated as a result of knowledge of the condition of an item from routine or continuous checking'. Corrective maintenance, initiated by a maintenance planning engineer after a report of cracks in a wall or overheating in a machine, noticed by a maintenance man during a preventive maintenance check, is condition-based maintenance. Condition reports arise from human observations, checks and tests, or from fixed instrumentation or alarm systems grouped under the name 'condition monitoring'. Condition monitoring has been recommended practice on aircraft engines for some years and has been successful in containing maintenance costs and preventing costly or dangerous failures.

Benefits to be expected from a condition monitoring programme include:

1 Reduced expenditure on preventive maintenance.
2 No unnecessary dismantling of plant items.
3 Less (or less serious) breakdowns.
4 Avoidance of consequential damage.

Expenditure on preventive maintenance can become excessive, particularly in the first applications of a planning system. Inspection routines can often be modified and reduced, especially when consistent reports of 'no work required' are received. The introduction of condition monitoring techniques provides for rationalization of the preventive maintenance schedules. In particular it is important to avoid unnecessary dismantling of plant or equipment. Partial dismantling or an unnecessary overhaul can be an expensive way of discovering that the item is perfectly alright, and often disturbs the running characteristics; increasing the wear rate or creating fault conditions. Condition monitoring determines the health of the asset (where possible) from an external inspection and by detection of incipient faults can reduce the frequency or effects of breakdowns. Finally, by detection of an incipient fault, consequential damage can be minimized. For example, if a faulty bearing in a high-speed compressor is discovered, the compressor can be stopped and the bearing changed before serious damage is done to castings and related components.

Condition monitoring also contributes to maintenance planning, maintenance cost reductions, health and safety programmes and to energy conservation. Maintenance planning is often assisted by advance warning of faults, so that the corrective work can be planned in advance and the task is classified as 'corrective' rather than 'emergency'. Pre-planning also allows for support to be organized in terms of access equipment, spare parts, technical information and any special-skills personnel. Pre-planning also means that work can often be done in normal hours to reduce workloads in unsocial hours. Advance planning ensures minimum work times and less overtime payments, thus reducing maintenance costs. Condition monitoring also contributes to health and safety by recognizing faults which may give rise to pollution or health hazards, also by indication of incipient faults which could produce danger conditions. Finally, condition monitoring can contribute to energy conservation by providing early warning of waste and inefficiency arising from faulty operation.

Levels of Monitoring

Condition monitoring can be considered at four levels:

Level 1 — Inspection monitoring based on the human senses, as in preventive maintenance schedules.

Level 2 — Assisted monitoring, using portable equipment.

Level 3 — Lubricant analysis and wear debris collection.

Level 4 — Fixed monitoring systems connected to alarm systems or data logging equipment.

The inspections at level 1 of the monitoring programme form part of the normal preventive maintenance schedules and are generally included in the daily and weekly activities. The inspectors are expected to use sight, hearing, touch and smell and to obtain a sensory impression of the condition of the asset. The senses may be assisted by magnifiers, viewing devices, temperature sensing strips or paints, stroboscopes, fixed instruments, or indicators. Whilst fixed monitoring systems can provide alarms or even analogue indications and trends, there is great value in skilled human observation at this level.

At level 2 the inspector is assisted by a range of portable test equipment to make a variety of measurements. Examples of the tests to be made and the types of equipment used are listed below:

Measurements	*Equipment*
Speed and running time	Tachometers, counters
Electrical quantities	Test meters
Fits and tolerances	Proximity testers
Temperature	Thermography
Vibration wear	Vibration analyser or shock pulse tester
Movement	Frequency analysis
Deterioration of materials	Radiography; Ultrasonics; Dye penetration.

This type of monitoring is applied to selected assets from the asset register for which a condition history file is built up. Quantities and characteristics are recorded and variations observed and interpreted. The technician can in effect view the internal components, without dismantling, test their working relationships and often predict the type and time of failure.

Level 3 monitoring is confined to lubricated items and consists of checks on component wear together with checks on contamination of the lubricant. Wear of components is usually indicated by metal particles and debris, which are floating in the lubricant and can be collected by a magnetic device. Contamination of the lubricant is detected by sampling and subsequent spectrometric analysis.

Fixed monitoring systems, as proposed for level 4 monitoring range from simple remote alarm systems to comprehensive data gathering systems based on mini-computers or micro-processors. A wide variety of contact points, transducers, accelerometers, counters and other sensors are employed. Data can be transmitted by wires directly to the display or can be electronically processed on a time-shared signal transmission system. Some fixed monitoring systems provide local alarm systems for critical items, some give general surveillance of a variety of sensors, some include general fire alarms, security, intruder detection, energy conservation and programming of essential services on a single, computer-controlled system. There is considerable economy when a fixed monitoring system is so arranged that it is not limited to a condition monitoring application, and the system cost can often be justified by multiple use. It is important to determine precise responsibilities for the interpretation of alarms and for subsequent actions, especially if the alarm indicators are supervised by telephone switchboard operators or other watchkeeping personnel.

Condition Monitoring Applications

A typical monitoring application is illustrated in Figure 9:1. Permanent indications were provided for:

1   Chilled water inlet temperature.
2   Chilled water outlet temperature.
3   Cold gas pressure and temperature.
4   Hot gas pressure and temperature.
5   Sea water inlet temperature.
6   Sea water outlet temperature.

Additional information can be obtained from:

1   Motor currents (3 motors) – fixed ammeters.
2   Bearings condition (3 motors, compressor, 2 pumps) – portable instruments for shock pulse or vibration monitoring.
3   Lubricant condition (2 pumps and compressor) – oil sampling, particle detection and analysis of oil samples.
4   Temperature, fire or smoke warning devices.

Selected signals can be sampled on a regular frequency, or continuously monitored by a scanning and alarm system using direct electrical wiring or electronic time division multiplexing for the signal transmissions.

A condition monitoring installation may be applied generally or can be introduced for an individual machine or group of machines which merit special attention. If applied generally, it is necessary to scan the asset register and to grade each asset in terms of:

1   Essential for monitoring.
2   Important for monitoring.
3   Desirable for monitoring.

It is then possible to apply monitoring techniques to the essential items on the register and to extend to the other assets as resources become available. In applications where a considerable proportion of the total resources are expended on programmes of preventive maintenance, reductions of 20% or more in these programmes are the objective, to give 3-year to 5-year paybacks on the installation costs. Payback expectations will generally be exceeded because of the additional benefits from reductions in consequential losses, loss-of-use or lost production, and repair costs. In applications where the total payback is expected in terms of loss reduction the payback time can be very short, although it is sometimes difficult to prove the connection between the new measures and the losses which might have occurred.

Analysis Techniques

Analysis of the vibration signals produced during the operation of a machine provide important evidence as to its 'health'. Most serious faults will produce increases in vibration level before complete failure and if detected in time will indicate the need to make an adjustment or repair before a breakdown occurs, see Figure 9:2. The signs of incipient failure will often be present long before this, though it may be necessary to employ specialised analysis techniques to detect these smaller variations in the vibration pattern and to diagnose the reason.

One such analysis technique is spectrum analysis in which recordings are made at regular intervals, each being compared with the previous recording or with an original recording used as a standard. It is of course most important that these 'signatures' as they are called are always prepared in the same manner, using the same probes and monitoring equipment, with the machine operating in the same mode, and using the identical test points on the machine. Figure 9:3 illustrates signatures recorded from a gearbox in which the shaft speeds are 50 Hz and 120 Hz. Signature (a) is the original, and signature (b), prepared one month later, shows an 11 dB increase at 120 Hz. This indicates deterioration in the performance of the high speed shaft. After balancing and re-alignment, the gearbox again operated satisfactorily, see signature (c). The frequency at which a change in the spectrum occurs can provide guidance to the source of the trouble, which is often related to the running speed. Figure 9:4 lists a number of faults and how they can be diagnosed with respect to frequency and direction.

Shock Pulse Monitoring

The shock pulse method (SPM) was first developed in Sweden and provides a technique for monitoring rolling element bearings so that they can be replaced when imminent failure is indicated. SPM measures the magnitude of mechanical impact which occurs when damage is present in a bearing and the bearing surfaces collide with this damage. Minor mechanical impacts occur in a new bearing because of surface roughness but the value of the mechanical impact over the working life of a bearing can increase 1,000 times. If the bearing is faulty when new, or is incorrectly assembled, the increased magnitude of mechanical impact will be obvious. Any increase in magnitude during the life of the bearing and caused by wear or damage will be detected and will provide a guide for replacement planning.

To measure the mechanical impact (or shock pulse) only, without influence from other vibration signals, a tuned piezo-electric transducer is used. When mechanical impact occurs the transducer resonates and produces a damped transient output superimposed on the low-frequency vibration signal. The magnitude of the transient signal is directly proportional to the magnitude of the impact. Electronic circuits are used to filter the vibration signals so that the transient can be measured and analysed. Typical SPM installations consist of transducers in various forms with portable or fixed monitors. The range of monitors includes the basic periodic monitor (Figure 9:5(a)), the portable diagnostic recorder (Figure 9:5(b)), and an installed preprogrammed surveillance unit. This latter unit compares the transient with a preprogrammed limit and can stop the machine or sound the alarm when the limit is exceeded.

Wear Debris Collection

Indications of wear in moving components can be given by wear debris, floating in lubrication or other liquid systems. Collection of this debris is usually achieved by use of filters or magnets, the latter being attached to drain plugs fitted with self-closing valves. Electric chip detectors consist of magnets with an electrical circuit which can be connected to an alarm for indication of a high rate of chip (particle) detection.

The three phases in the life of a machine are shown in Figure 9:6 as running-in, normal operation and failure period. In phase 1 any surface roughness is worn away and the resulting particles tend to be small and in large quantities, with the rate of particle production reducing over the period. In phase 2, the wear rate is expected to be low, with small particles produced in small quantities. In phase 3 some break-up of a surface may occur and this tends to be a continuing process with the particles causing further stress and with even larger particles produced.

Electric chip detectors provide a horizontal failure detection capability (HFD) in which any level of particle deposition which is above a normal expectation will produce an alarm. Magnetic chip detectors, which are removed for inspection and cleaning on a regular basis, provide vertical failure detection (VFD). If located correctly, these detectors can catch more than 75% of the available particles in a liquid system.

Lubricant Analysis

Abnormal wear rates in lubricated machinery, contamination of lubricants and indications of lubrication efficiency can be confirmed by examination of oil samples. Figure 9:7 illustrates the reporting document used when this service is obtained from the laboratory of an oil company. For maximum effectiveness and history generation these samples should be submitted on a regular basis.

A list of the analytical data reported includes:

1   Wear elements – iron, aluminium, copper, chromium, tin, silicon dust.
2   Viscosity.
3   Water content.

Additional tests can be applied to indicate:

1   Fuel dilution.
2   Fuel soot.
3   Anti-freeze content, etc.

Fixed Monitoring Systems

A typical fixed monitoring system is illustrated by Figure 9:8. A range of important items of plant and equipment on the site are monitored through sensors attached to the plant items or included in their circuits. For completeness and economy, the system is also used for fire detection and to provide some analogue signals showing plant states.

The sensors in a particular geographical area of the site are connected by electrical wiring to an electronic unit, which is in turn connected to a common time-shared line and to annunciators in the engineering and administration offices. In a time-shared system, each sensor is sampled in turn and the resulting signals are transmitted in turn along a common line. Thus the costs and the problems of providing individual wiring from each sensor to the master annunciators are avoided.

Centralized Surveillance

In a comprehensive monitoring system, these electronic techniques, using microprocessors and visual display units (VDU) can provide the following services:

1   Condition monitoring of important plant.
2   Fire detection.
3   Intruder alarms.
4   Theft detection.
5   Environment control.
6   Energy conservation.

A typical control centre for this type of installation is illustrated in Figure 9:9 and consists of visual display units, a keyboard, data logger and printer. The printer can provide both management information and maintenance job sheets.

The payback for such a system can occur in any of the categories of use which are listed above. However, rising fuel costs have focussed attention on energy conservation and, in this category alone, the cost of the system may be recovered in two years or less. In practice, condition monitoring and energy conservation are closely linked. For example, a fault in an air conditioning system can be detected immediately if the plant item is monitored; this not only speeds the repair action but prevents the waste of fuel which could occur if the fault remained until the next preventive maintenance inspection.

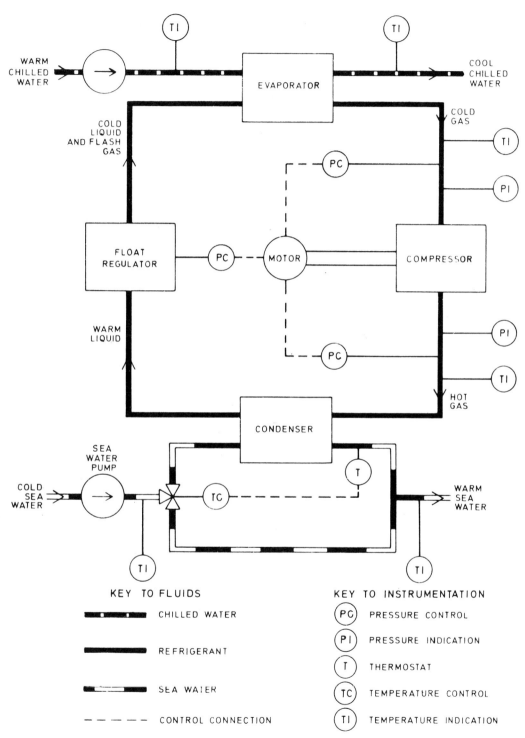

Figure 9:1 **System diagram showing pressure and temperature indicators**

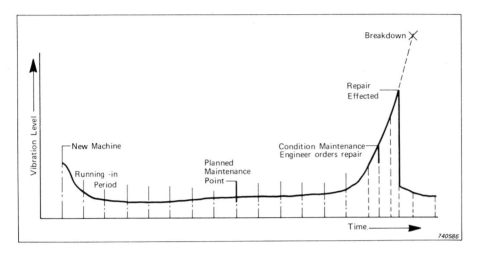

A typical "Bathtub" curve showing how planned maintenance often schedules part replacement a long time before increased vibration level detected by regular condition monitoring indicates the need for replacement

Figure 9:2   Vibration level/repair time relationships

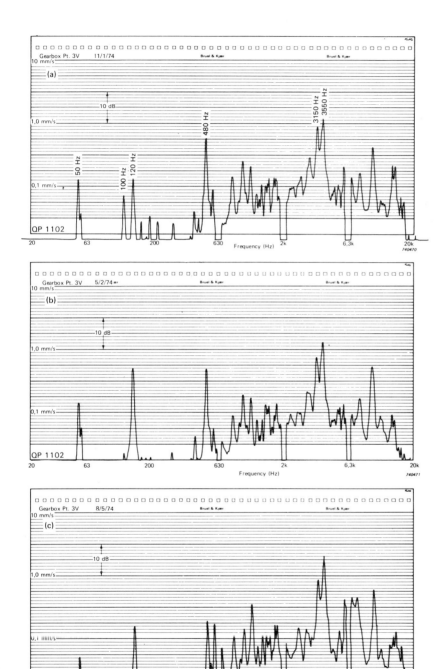

Figure 9:3   Gearbox vibration spectra

VIBRATION TROUBLE SHOOTING CHART

Nature of Fault	Frequency of Dominant Vibration (Hz=rpm/60)	Direction	Remarks
Rotating Members out of Balance	1 x rpm	Radial	A common cause of excess vibration in machinery
Misalignment & Bent Shaft	Usually 1 x rpm Often 2 x rpm Sometimes 3&4 x rpm	Radial & Axial	A common fault
Damaged Rolling Element Bearings (Ball, Roller, etc.)	Impact rates for the individual bearing components* Also vibrations at very high frequencies (20 to 60 kHz)	Radial & Axial	Uneven vibration levels, often with shocks. *Impact-Rates: Contact Angle β — Ball Dia (BD) — Pitch Dia (PD). Impact Rates f (Hz): For Outer Race Defect $f(Hz) = \frac{n}{2} f_r (1 - \frac{BD}{PD} \cos\beta)$ For Inner Race Defect $f(Hz) = \frac{n}{2} f_r (1 + \frac{BD}{PD} \cos\beta)$ For Ball Defect $f(Hz) = \frac{PD}{BD} f_r [1 - \frac{BD^2}{PD^2} \cos^2\beta]$ n = number of balls or rollers f_r = relative rev./s between inner & outer races 740561
Journal Bearings Loose in Housings	Sub-harmonics of shaft rpm, exactly 1/2 or 1/3 x rpm	Primarily Radial	Looseness may only develop at operating speed and temperature (eg. turbomachines).
Oil Film Whirl or Whip in Journal Bearings	Slightly less than half shaft speed (42% to 48%)	Primarily Radial	Applicable to high-speed (eg. turbo) machines.
Hysteresis Whirl	Shaft critical speed	Primarily Radial	Vibrations excited when passing through critical shaft speed are maintained at higher shaft speeds. Can sometimes be cured by checking tightness of rotor components.
Damaged or worn gears	Tooth meshing frequencies (shaft rpm x number of teeth) and harmonics	Radial & Axial	Sidebands around tooth meshing frequencies indicate modulation (eg. eccentricity) at frequency corresponding to sideband spacings. Normally only detectable with very narrow-band analysis.
Mechanical Looseness	2 x rpm and 0,5, 1,5, 2,5, 3,5, etc.		
Faulty Belt Drive	1, 2, 3 & 4 x rpm of belt	Radial	
Unbalanced Reciprocating Forces and Couples	1 x rpm and/or multiples for higher order unbalance	Primarily Radial	
Increased Turbulence	Blade & Vane passing frequencies and harmonics	Radial & Axial	Increasing levels indicate increasing turbulence
Electrically Induced Vibrations	1 x rpm or 1 or 2 times sychronous frequency	Radial & Axial	Should disappear when turning off the power

740609

Figure 9:4   Diagnostic chart for vibration analysis

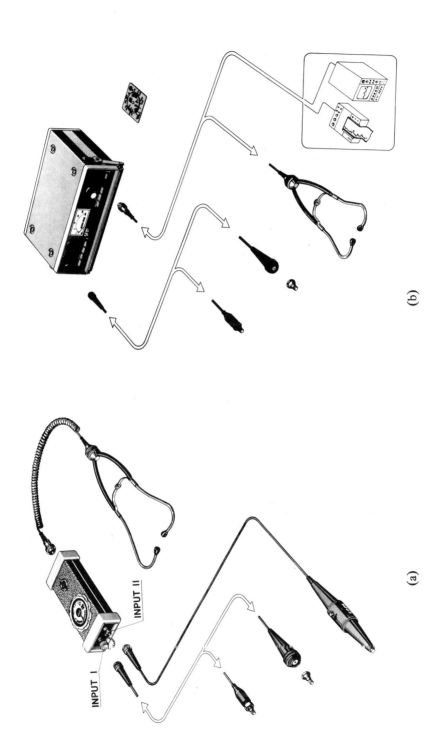

INPUT I

INPUT II

(a)

(b)

Figure 9:5 Shock pulse monitoring instruments

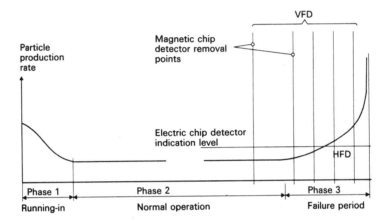

Figure 9:6   Particle production in a gas turbine

Industrial Lubrication Service

CONDITION MONITORING SERVICE
WEAR METAL ASSESSMENT REPORT

Lubrication

Customer_____ Unit/Make/Type_____

Site Address _____ Serial No. _____

_____ Application _____

Attn. of: _____ Phone _____ Fuel Used_____ Oil Used _____

Lab No.	Date	Since Oil Change		P.P.M.							Vis.	Water			A-Code
		Hrs	Oil Added	Fe	Al	Sn	Cu	Si	Cr						

Comments on latest smple:

Figure 9:7   Metal detection report from lubricant analysis

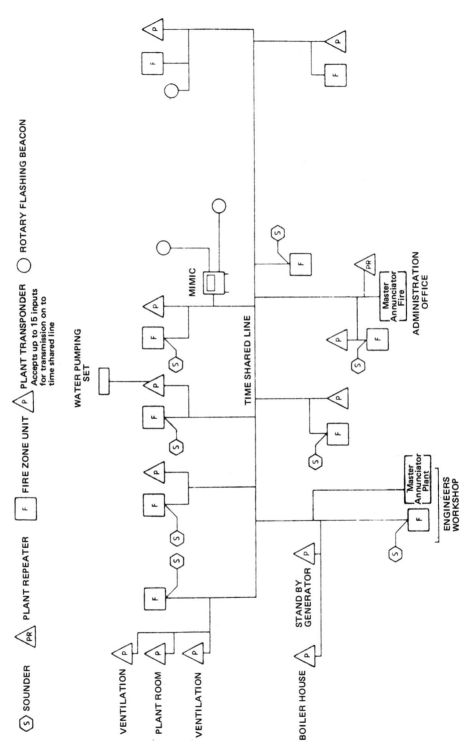

Figure 9:8   Schematic diagram for fire alarm and plant monitor system using common time-shared line cables

Figure 9:9   Control centre for surveillance system

10

Procurement

Considerable care is necessary when purchasing industrial plant and equipment of any kind. The person making the procurement must investigate thoroughly the various aspects described in this chapter as the successful and profitable operation of the plant is dependent to a large extent upon his ability to not only buy the right equipment at the right price but also to evaluate the suitability of the equipment for its proposed usage. Careful procurement can produce the following benefits:

1 Simple installation.
2 Minimum commissioning time.
3 Rapid training of operators and maintainers.
4 High utilization with minimum 'downtime'.
5 Long life.
6 Low operating cost.
7 Easy maintenance at low cost.
8 Minimum investment in tools and spare parts.

The buyer can protect the investment, to obtain high utilization and ensure an adequate return on the capital employed by giving attention to:

1 Maintainability.
2 Reliability.
3 Installation and commissioning.
4 Product support.
5 Costs.

These headings are defined below.

Definitions

Maintainability

The designers of all physical assets should ensure that their designs provide:

1   A minimum maintenance requirement.
2   Rapid fault-diagnosis and repair.
3   Low maintenance and repair costs.

Assets which conform to these three objectives possess 'maintainability'.

Reliability

Reliability is shown by the length of time between breakdowns in service. The best suppliers have quality and reliability departments which ensure that the materials, the manufacturing or construction processes, and the final product are all of a high standard of reliability.

Installation and commissioning

The signs of an unsatisfactory purchase usually become obvious during the installation and commissioning period. This is the time when the asset is delivered, connected to other services and put into operation.

Product support

This term is defined in Chapter 8.

Costs

The total cost is the cost of the asset plus the costs of delivery, installation or construction, commissioning and product support.

Benefits

Some of the benefits to be obtained through careful procurement are explained below. It will be seen that ability of the procurement officer is extremely important if the assets are to give good service and operate economically. The procurement officer must be prepared to consult his maintenance colleagues as necessary.

Installation

The problems of transportation, lifting, foundations, access, and essential services, must be understood before final contracts are placed. Site construction costs can be very large and drawings should be obtained so that these costs can be estimated as part of the total cost. The need for services must be assessed so that electricity, compressed air, etc. can be arranged. Questions such as 'Can the compressed air be provided from an existing compressor or is an additional one necessary?' need to be answered and technical information from the vendor is required. Items to check are:—

Transportation	Lifting gear
Site access	Building access
Foundations	Noise, vibration, pollution
Supplies (air, oil, water, gas, electricity)	Waste disposal

Plant must be easily installed and, if it is part of a production line which could be subjected to replanning, must be reasonably easy to relocate. Care given to this point can give savings in engineering manpower and reductions in the costs of lost production during replanning.

Although new plant is frequently installed and commissioned by vendor engineers it is necessary to ensure that sufficient technical information is supplied to enable the plant engineers to become fully conversant with it and as independent as possible. Dependence upon the vendor engineers during a breakdown leads to lost production unless they are permanently on the site and this is expensive. A large investment in plant is only safeguarded when the plant engineers fully understand it for maintenance purposes. Thus the procurement officer should ensure that complete technical instructions are given and that these are printed and supplied as a permanent record. Instructions given verbally to plant engineers are no safeguard against:

1 Accidents to trained staff.
2 Staff changes.
3 The inability of some engineers to train their assistants and to pass on knowledge.

Commissioning

Commissioning is always easier when plant is purchased from a competent vendor. First, the plant will be packaged properly so that it arrives in good repair. Second, it will have comprehensive instructions for the operator and the engineers. Third, it will be provided with a specification for operational and performance tests. Most reliable manufacturers test their products to a 'quality assurance' specification written by their quality and reliability department. This specification is used in the factory to ensure that the plant is of the right quality before delivery. The same specification, or a modified version of it, should be used by the plant engineer as an acceptance specification during commissioning. With the specification will be performance records as proof of the factory tests. The product support requirement (Figure 10:1) includes technical handbooks, manuals and training aids. Depending upon the complexity of the plant, the training of operators and engineers will be possible with the use of the handbooks only or through training courses for which training aids or devices are necessary. These may include training books, charts, films, transparencies or models. The information should conform to that given in the technical manuals or maintenance schedules, in general compatibility and also in standardization of technical terms.

Minimum downtime

Downtime is the time in which the plant is not available for production because of a need for maintenance or repair. Downtime can be caused by a breakdown of the plant, or by a failure of electricity or some other supply, or by a shutdown period for preventive maintenance.

Preventive maintenance usually consists of:

1   Lubrication and inspection.
2   Periodic overhaul.

Lubrication and inspection periods should be detailed in the maintenance schedules provided in the product support package. Many plant items are designed so that this work can be done without downtime, with the plant still working. The overhaul periods for the plant should also be specified so that arrangements may be made for a shutdown period during which the plant may be disassembled, cleaned, worn parts replaced and finally reassembled.

It is essential that the technical instructions provided with the plant contain full instructions for preventive maintenance including the frequency of lubrication, grades of lubricant, inspection procedures, overhaul instructions (with illustrations) and spare parts lists. Maintenance instructions for overhaul should indicate which parts should be replaced at each overhaul, also instructions for the measurement and inspection of the parts which have been replaced. Good parts can then be returned to the stores and worn parts can be disposed of.

The time taken for preventive maintenance, whether it is frequent lubrication and inspection or whether it is for overhaul, should be discussed with the vendor. If some doubts appear about the quality of the plant engineers to do this work within the predicted time then the necessary training must be provided. The procurement officer must always allow the plant engineer access to the technical information (manuals, etc.) to be provided by the vendor so that he can examine their usefulness to him.

Long life

The procurement officer must assure himself of the ability of the plant to give long service. This is closely linked with 'reliability'. Much can be determined from an advance study of the plant by the plant engineer who must consider whether the plant is designed for long service with a continued availability of spare parts from the manufacturer or whether the vendor's policy is to make frequent changes of design with built-in redundancy. Reference can be made to other users of plant from this particular vendor. If the policy is to make frequent changes without adequate servicing support for the preceding designs, then the vendor has to be reconsidered.

Low operating cost

The vendor should be asked for predictions of operating costs and his approach to this problem will indicate whether he has adequately assessed this before selling his product. Operating costs in each year will include:

> Interest on capital cost (total cost, as defined earlier).
> Cost of operating labour (number and grades of staff).
> Cost of maintenance.
> Depreciation of machine.
> Cost of downtime.
> Cost of space and services for machine.

Considerable variations are found in these costs.

Cost of maintenance

This is not a simple calculation. Among the many factors to be taken into account are:

> The quality of the technical information and training given.
> The standing investment in spare parts stock.
> The consumption of spares and lubricants per annum.
> The numbers and grades of maintenance staff required.
> The maintainability of the design itself.
> The reliability of the design.

The first point is very important and is dealt with in detail under 'Product support' later in this chapter.

Minimum investment in tools and spare parts

It is sometimes found that it is very costly to change vendors solely to satisfy lowest tender requirements. If previous plant is satisfactory and satisfies all the requirements it does not always benefit the user to change to another supplier to save a small percentage on the purchase price. Not only does a new type of plant require further investment in special tools and spare parts but also the maintenance staff have to learn new techniques.

The new vendor must be investigated in all respects before a decision is made in terms of initial cost only. An important factor for consideration is the cost of any special tools and non-standard spare parts. Vital production will depend on these spare parts and if the new machines are very different from other machines it will not be possible to interchange spare parts, when breakdowns occur, in order to restore operations.

Maintainability

Buildings, plant and equipment should be designed so that maintenance is as easy as possible and so that much routine maintenance is 'designed-out'. Design-out maintenance (DOM) is well-known practice; a typical example is the use of sealed bearings to remove the need for lubrication. However, some maintenance will always be needed, some faults will occur, and some repair will be necessary. The purchasing officer can make sure that this is minimal by asking questions like the following or by using his maintenance manager or an engineering consultant to ask them:

Has a reliability and maintainability study been made for the plant? Such a study will produce MTBF (Mean Times Before Failure) and MTTR (Mean Times To Repair) predictions for the whole plant and for individual items. Critical parts can then be identified, appropriate spare parts can be stored and other plans made to cope with possible failures.

Do the designers employ DOM techniques?

Are arrangements made for fast fault diagnosis when there is a breakdown? The time taken to locate a fault is added to the repair time to produce the total downtime so the fault diagnosis must be as fast as possible. Among the points to look for are:

1   Undue dependencies (a whole process depending on one small part which could easily fail).
2   Too few test positions which are marked for recognition and are easily accessible for tests to be made.
3   Requirement for special test gear which is not provided with the plant.

Fault diagnosis is fast and simple if the designer provides facilities in his design.

Another important aspect of maintenance is condition monitoring. This may range from simple running tests for accuracy on a machine tool to a vibration test position provided on a generator or compressor. In many installations, performance checks or vibration monitoring are used to provide a warning when maintenance is required. It is a good thing to provide for this when buying a new plant.

Does a lubrication/inspection schedule exist? Many designers have to be disciplined into seeing the plant from the users' position. It is for them to consider the problems of lubrication and inspection and to prepare the procedural instructions and the recommended frequencies.

Do maintenance schedules exist? These have to show the maintenance philosophy for the plant. For example, if it is necessary to take it to pieces after every 50,000 hours of running then precise instructions and illustrations are needed.

The spare parts policy requires examination. Is there a list of recommended spare parts? Which items are already in the stores? Money can be saved by buying machinery which uses standard parts. Not only is the cost of the total spares holding reduced but parts can be changed between machines to maintain production when one machine is out of service. What are the lead times for the non-standard spares items? A 'lead time' is the time between ordering a spare part and its arrival on site. If this is too long, then arrangements must be made for local manufacture and the vendor must supply detailed workshop drawings for this. Are component identities clearly marked? This applies particularly to electrical and electronic systems. Markings on the components in any type of system must correspond with the spare parts list.

What special tools and lifting gear are required? The vendor must realize that this is part of the total cost of the plant and the procurement officer must ensure that his plant engineers have the opportunity of checking that the procurement is comprehensive in this respect.

The maintenance labour requirements of the plant should be examined. In much plant of good design, a large amount of operator maintenance is possible. Some fault indicators may also be included to guide the operator in simple fault diagnosis. This helps to improve utilization of the machine; firstly, because operator maintenance can be scheduled by the operator into non-productive periods and secondly, fault diagnosis by the operator avoids the waiting period until a maintenance man arrives. Another important point is the reliance on vendor maintenance, which also introduces a waiting period. Most maintenance can be performed by the plant engineers if sufficient technical information is provided.

The final point on the list concerns vendor maintenance contracts. These are necessary and useful in certain procurements (computers, for example) and the vendor's proposals should be discussed with the plant engineers.

Quality assurance

As stated earlier, the best vendors have quality and reliability departments whose task is to ensure that the incoming materials, the product at the various stages of construction or manufacture, and the final product as delivered to the user is of high quality. The procurement officer should ask about the quality system of the vendor and in particular the following questions:

1   Is quality control applied at all stages of materials inputs, processing and manufacture?
2   Are quality assurance specifications available? These are the final specifications to which the product is tested before it leaves the factory. Copies of these should be provided for use as acceptance specifications when the plant is

delivered to the site, although in some circumstances the quality requirements might be reduced slightly from those required by the stringent test conditions in the factory.

Delivery and installation

Some of the problems at this time have been described earlier but the checklist in Appendix 1 contains reminders about:

1   Installation drawings — these should be made available when a quotation is submitted so that assessments can be made about the installation problems and the costs.
2   The power, weight and size requirements should also be available for discussions.
3   Any special foundations must be considered and costs.
4   In the case of production-line machinery it is necessary to consider if the equipment can be moved easily. A long wait for special equipment or for vendor engineers can make factory planning very difficult and inflexible.

Product support

The supply of correct product support information is vital to the success of any plant or machinery installation. Figure 10:2 shows how a support system is arranged for a complete plant installation. Not only should the support documentation be evaluated to ensure that it includes all necessary information for training, operation, preventive maintenance, fault diagnosis, overhaul and spare parts but it should be examined to see if it is suitable for the particular application. If it is in a foreign language and not translated, or if there are too many words and not enough useful diagrams, or if it describes advanced technologies with which staff are not familiar, then it cannot fulfil its purpose. That purpose is to give full information, correct information and useful information in the shortest possible reading time. For complete plant installations the question of balance between the treatment of the various plant items is also important. The balance is not correct if the manufacturers of small plant items supply a great deal of information whilst suppliers of larger plant give very little. The main contractor should ensure that all plant items are supported to the appropriate level in accordance with their operational and maintenance requirements.

Ideally, a specialist product support company should be employed by the main contractor, or a product support consultant engaged by the procurement authority to ensure that enough support is given to safeguard the investment in plant. Typical questions to ask are:

Will complete installation information be supplied at (or at a specified time before) delivery?

Will operators and maintainers receive training? The need for a long training period is sometimes brought about by poor design of the plant and the procurement officer, with the help of the manager of maintenance, has to decide if the training is adequate for the particular plant. In some circumstances, where the plant is clearly marked and is provided with illustrated handbooks, no formal training will be necessary. However, on a process plant, training in start-up, shutdown and safety procedures usually requires the supply of training aids and programmes. The tendency of many plant vendors to train staff only by providing engineers to give personal instruction during commissioning must be rejected. Unless permanent training information is provided the investment is not safeguarded against personnel changes, accidents to key personnel and other difficulties.

Will operator instructions be available with the installation? Whether training is given or not, written operating instructions are necessary.

Will maintenance information be available immediately after installation? Typical items required are:

1   Maintenance manual – this should contain
     (*a*) Operating instructions (unless supplied separately).
     (*b*) Operator maintenance routines (unless supplied separately).
     (*c*) Description of how plant works.
     (*d*) Safety procedures.
     (*e*) Fault diagnosis charts.
     (*f*) Maintenance schedules (unless supplied separately).
     (*g*) Overhaul instructions with full illustrations.
     (*h*) Spares lists (unless supplied separately).
2   Spare parts manual, fully illustrated.
3   Lists of recommended spare parts for stock.
4   The lubrication plan.
5   Maintenance schedules for preventive maintenance.
6   Circuit and other diagrams.

It is not easy to describe the precise type of information required but the plant engineer will know by inspection if it is suitable. It is important to receive the information with the plant so that it can be quickly evaluated.

Typical points to look for are:

1   Is information clearly presented with block diagrams, flow charts and other drawings to complement the text?
2   Does the spares list correspond to the technical manual with the same names used for parts?
3   Are the operating instructions and operator maintenance instructions clear? Ideally, they should be produced separately on plastic sheet or card or as a pocket book.
4   Are preventive maintenance schedules, with frequencies, given for lubrication, inspection and overhaul maintenance? The instructions should be clear, with

diagrams, and are best produced separately on card or plastic sheet.

5   Has information been prepared so that each part is complete? Cross references between pages cause much delay and the manual soon wears out.

6   Has translation into the correct working language been done (if equipment is foreign-made) and is the translation correct?

Will the maintenance manual contain full instructions, with illustrations, for overhaul of the plant? This must include disassembly, repair or replacement of parts, reassembly and testing. The names of the parts and, if possible, the illustrations should be the same as for the spare parts list. The maintenance manual should make the maintenance policy clear and should provide full instructions for the policy to be successfully implemented.

Is all the technical documentation user-orientated and suitable for the personnel employed? The manuals must be immediately useful to the workers, they must be comprehensive, and they must contain enough data to make the engineer independent of outside sources.

Are the special tools available? The best vendors export the servicing equipment with the plant so that there is no confusion.

Are the recommended spares available?

Will production drawings be supplied to permit local manufacture of non-standard spare parts? This is quite important as non-availability of these drawings poses the same problem as non-availability of the spares themselves.

Costs

To prevent subsequent misunderstandings it is necessary during procurement to define clearly what is being sold and for how much.

Prices should be stated for:

1   The machine, delivered and installed.
2   The spares package, complete.
3   The spares package, less any items already stocked by the plant engineer.
4   The special tools and lifting gear.
5   Product support (training, technical manuals, spares lists, maintenance schedules)

Other questions to be asked include the following.

Is the machine similar to a previous purchase? If so are some of the spare parts duplicated and can the spares costs be reduced?

Does the maintenance manager approve the purchase? No procurement officer should buy without adequate consultation about the purchase. The engineers, or the consultants, may observe something which the buyer has not had time to notice; for example, some machinery is designed in such a way that maintenance is difficult and some machinery uses special motors which are difficult and expensive to rewind if they become damaged.

Is the machine interchangeable with existing plant to facilitate shutdown maintenance? If machines can be changed over, production can continue with one undergoing maintenance. Another advantage is that, with different faults on two machines, spare parts may be exchanged to keep one machine working.

Bearing in mind the comments of the maintainers, or the project consultants, upon the preceding points is it desirable to buy the lowest tender offer and what is the extra cost of buying in accordance with their recommendations? (Enough has been said to indicate that procurement on lowest tender without regard to other factors can be expensive even in the short term.)

Finally, will the vendor accept full penalties on these other procurement items as on the asset itself? If he will not then he is not sure of his ability to meet your requirements for manuals, spares, product support, etc. in the stated times. After all he knows better than you do what his firm is like and what its policies in these matters are, and if he cannot trust it, neither should you.

Rules for Procurement

Certain generalizations have been made in an attempt to deal with all kinds of installations (plant, equipment, machines and instrumentation). Some interpretation will be necessary in a particular situation and the best procedure is:

1 Use the checklist as far as it can be applied (see Appendix 1).
2 Consult the maintenance engineer or a technical adviser.
3 When in doubt get specialist help from an engineering consultant.
4 When previous experience shows that a vendor is not producing the right technical information, call in a specialist consultant in technical communication.

Capital Project Management

The stages in the life cycle of a new capital project may be defined as follows:

Conception	formulation of project idea.
Approval	preliminary discussion and agreement on study.
Formulation	study of various implementation methods.
Evaluation	decision on implementation.
Procurement	selection of vendors.
Design	vendor's development of concept.
Construction	manufacture of hardware.
Installation	construction and installation often run concurrently.
Commissioning	often referred to as 'start-up'.
Hand-over	buyer accepts responsibility.
Proving	testing under normal conditions.

The handover is sometimes partial and proving is necessary before final acceptance by the buyer.

The idea for a project arrives by formal or informal channels. The reading of a technical magazine by an engineer may bring new processes or new equipment to the company's attention, a chance remark to one director by another may arouse interest in a new product, or the company as part of its technical or product range development may commission a study by its own staff or by a consultant regarding its next development programme. In the case of domestic-type installations, suggestions may come from within or from external consultants, architects, etc. If time and money is to be expended in a study of the idea, approval is sought and budgetary provisions made for a detailed study of implementation methods. This study might entail consideration of:

1   Life cycle costs, and return on investment for the existing installation (if applicable).
2   Predictions for these after the project has been implemented.
3   Predictions after implementation by the various methods available.
4   The development costs, operating costs, maintenance costs and possible problems arising if new technologies are introduced.
5   The possibilities for achieving similar results (technical or financial) without introducing new techniques and non-standard plant.
6   The comparative effects of siting the new plant on existing sites or as a completely new installation.

When increased output is the sole objective for the idea, a number of factors require investigation. First of these must be an examination of the utilization of existing plant and whether or not this can be improved. Detailed studies may be necessary on administration, production and maintenance methods, also on plant layout, handling and other factors contributing to full utilization. Innovation costs money in terms of long commissioning times, staff training, spares investment, improvement of services, loss of flexibility in operation, and increased first-year operating and maintenance costs. The introduction of sophisticated equipment may entail the handover of maintenance to vendor engineers on contract.

The operating and maintenance aspects must be fully considered and the maintenance manager consulted. The effect on maintenance investments for a separate plant or an extension of an existing plant may include increases from the following sources:

Item	*Separate plant*	*Extension*
Maintenance.	New maintenance building or	Possibly a zone workshop.
Accommodation.	floor space allocation in new buildings.	Additional floor space if existing accommodation inadequate.

Item	*Separate plant*	*Extension*
Workshop plant, tools and access equipment.	An appropriate proportion of the project costs based on existing knowledge.	Equipment for zone workshop with an evaluation of use to be made of existing main workshop. Transport between zones.
Staff requirements.	Manager or assistant manager and staff.	Supervisors and additional staff.
Installation and commissioning.	Allocation of maintenance management and staff during installation phase to achieve familiarity with new plant.	
Product support.	The capital cost and charges arising from the documentation and training aspects.	
Spares provisioning.	A complete range of plant spares plus standard stocks of parts and materials.	The recommended range of spares, less any adjustments for rationalization.
Staff training.	Requirements for special staff training, above the machine training provided by the vendor, if new techniques are introduced.	
Maintenance. Consultancy.	Development of maintenance policy, organization of effective product support and introduction of maintenance planning.	

Typical operating costs for the maintenance department will include:

1   Salaries for the additional personnel.
2   Social payments for the additional personnel.
3   Spares and materials costs.
4   Depreciation of buildings occupied by the maintenance staff.
5   Overhead charges, insurances, etc.
6   Depreciation of workshop plant, tools, spares and equipment.
7   Subcontract costs.

In the first year of a new installation additional costs incurred may include:

1   Excessive overtime working during familiarization period.
2   Increased use of vendor service engineers.
3   High spares consumption caused by start-up problems and also some wastage.
4   Further training requirements for maintenance staff.

In addition, low utilization rates and increased downtime costs are sometimes a feature of first-year working.

In a typical maintenance budget (although actual budgets vary enormously) the approximate allocations are:

Cost item	Allowance
Materials and subcontract	25%
Personnel – total costs	40%
Depreciation and overheads	25%
Other items	10%

The total maintenance budget may be 7 to 10 per cent of the total investment in an industrial installation.

Depreciation charges for plant vary from 8 to 15 per cent and for transport from 15 to 25 per cent. A maintenance budget for the first year of operation may rise to 20 per cent above normal because of the first-year expenditure items listed earlier.

The maintenance manager appointed to a new project may, if appointed at an early stage, request a number of studies by the project engineers. Typical studies are:

1　Study of vendor assistance proposals.
　　(*a*)　Should vendor's proposals for training etc. be accepted?
　　(*b*)　Should training and product support be subcontracted to specialist firms?
　　(*c*)　Are independent commissioning engineers to be used?
　　(*d*)　Is a vendor servicing contract desirable?
2　Study of operating and maintenance requirements.
　　(*a*)　Will required utilization be achieved?
　　(*b*)　What numbers and grades of manpower are necessary?
　　(*c*)　Have all services requirements be clarified?
　　(*d*)　Are all aspects of maintenance support provided for?
3　Study of maintenance planning and control systems.
　　(*a*)　Is planned maintenance provided for?
　　(*b*)　Which control method will be used?
　　(*c*)　Can this plant and others be combined to justify more sophisticated planning systems?
　　(*d*)　Will a maintenance consultant be appointed?
4　Study of spare-parts requirements.
　　(*a*)　Are vendor recommendations acceptable?
　　(*b*)　Will drawings be supplied for local spares manufacture?
　　(*c*)　Is the spares investment at acceptable level?
　　(*d*)　Are original sources of spares known?
　　(*e*)　Are spares compatible with existing stocks?
5　Study of monitoring techniques.
　　(*a*)　Is vibration analysis or other condition monitoring included?
　　(*b*)　Is remote control or centralized surveillance desirable?

(c)   Are adequate alarms provided?

(d)   Are fault-diagnosis methods provided for?

These and other studies set the pattern for subsequent maintenance of the plant at an acceptable utilization factor.

Procurement has already received much attention in this book and rightly so, for a wrong decision, or a failure to make a suitable contract at this time may give rise to problems extending over years of plant utilization. The total involvement of the maintenance manager in new project work is essential if effective maintenance is to be a feature of future years. If effective maintenance planning and control methods are used in an existing maintenance department, the maintenance manager should be available for participation in new work programmes. If a completely new installation is being planned, the maintenance manager must be recruited at an early phase.

Figure 10:3 lists a number of factors contributing to efficiency in the maintenance department which merit attention when a capital project is planned. Possibly the most important is item 3 — the inclusion of the support items within the penalty clauses.

It is the responsibility of the project planner, with assistance from the maintenance manager or chief engineer, to set the pattern for a controlled situation in the maintenance department. The introduction of planning methods, control systems and effective support organizations depends upon the disciplines imposed at procurement, firstly, upon the planner to know what is required and to provide for it, and secondly upon the plant suppliers (vendors) to meet their obligations. Even if rigid procurement rules are applied the supply of equipment and, in particular, the product support items can be months or years off target. It is the responsibility of the project planner to discipline all concerned into a successful project.

This may often entail the appointment of a terotechnology consultant (see Figure 10:4) at the formulation stage or later as required (Reference 6). His duties would include:

Formulation stage — evaluation of maintenance aspects of various methods and
   development of monitoring and maintenance policies.

Procurement stage — vetting of contracts for maintenance aspects.

Design and construction — monitor maintainability aspects.

Installation and commissioning — evaluate product support activity by vendors and
   enforce contract provisions. Develop planned maintenance system, plant records,
   and technical information system. Arrange training programmes.

Post-commissioning — finalize technical information system, review planning system,
   update as necessary.

Balanced Capital Project Information

Care is necessary on capital work.to ensure that a balance is maintained between the maintenance policies, product support policies and customer service methods of the various contractors and subcontractors. This is especially important when a major project costing perhaps several millions of pounds is split into three or four major subcontracts, each backed by many other suppliers. Coordination is essential with particular attention to the maintenance aspects. Taking maintenance manuals as an example, the manufacturer of a large piece of process equipment may supply a few typed sheets, whilst an instrument manufacturer provides a 30-page descriptive manual. This state of unbalance can be observed throughout all aspects of plant supply and the buyer's representatives, whether they be house engineers or consultant advisers, have to attempt to restore the balance. When maintenance planning is taking place the availability of balanced vendor recommendations reduces the cost of scheduling for maintenance. A balanced and coordinated spares policy is also important, the recommendations for one item, such as ball bearings for example, varying widely between suppliers.

Commissioning

The commissioning task can be interpreted in various ways, ranging from a simple start-up and test operation to a complete design, construction and suitability study. In the first case the start-up procedures provided by the vendors are checked out and running tests made to ensure that the plant conforms with the acceptance specification. In the second case a preliminary study may be made of such items as:

1 Reliability of components and of systems.
2 Quality of construction and installation.
3 Maintainability (access, diagnostic features, etc.).
4 Design-out-maintenance features.
5 Operability (human factors, skills levels, training).
6 Safety aspects.

Frequently the start-up and test aspects of commissioning are left to the equipment vendors but this can be unsatisfactory if:

1 Vendor staff may be preconditioned to testing in the factory environment, or
2 Minor modifications can be incorporated by vendor personnel and not be adequately documented.

For these and other reasons commissioning contracts are frequently given to independent commissioning and testing consultants, who work on a fixed-price basis and ensure that client requirements are met.

Ideally, the commissioning consultants should be employed at the very beginning of the project so that they can be most effective in analysing the design and in applying their experience in visualizing the practical application of the design so that technical feedback is made to the designers with the objective of reducing on-site modification activity and reducing the actual commissioning period. The use of commissioning consultants is not restricted to large capital projects and they are frequently used for individual boilers, air conditioning plants, etc. A typical scale of fees is given below.

Capital cost of plant	Commissioning charges
£15,000 to £50,000	2%
£50,000 to £500,000	1.5%
£500,000 to £1,500,000	1%
£1,500,000 plus	0.75%

On a normal start-up task the functions of the commissioning consultant will be:

1. Examining all project drawings, specifications, manuals, etc.
2. Specifying the requirements for commissioning.
3. Agreeing the work programme with the contractor.
4. Pre-commissioning inspection.
5. Start-up and testing in accordance with specification.
6. Proving to the client that item 5 is satisfactory.
7. Providing defect reports (if applicable).
8. Preparing the final performance report.

The commissioning charges mentioned above would not normally include provision for further testing following any modifications arising from item 7.

Handover

The handover of an installation from the vendors and commissioning engineers is often an abrupt process resulting in the maintenance staff taking over responsibility for equipment on which they have little experience and have inadequate information. A breakdown in the early days of plant life can then produce lengthy downtime and sometimes a high spares wastage as maintenance men apply basic knowledge only to problems on specialist equipment. There has been trade-union criticism of management in this respect and some sympathy can be felt for this view. Without doubt the maintenance management function includes the management of a handover in such a way that training, technical manuals and spares are made available and that some familiarization is attempted. Should the situation at installation and commissioning be such that plainly the desired state for handing over is not likely to be achieved, the maintenance manager may recruit a maintenance consultant or a specialist organization to improve the position.

Post-Commissioning Services

Also known as post-design services, these are services provided by the vendor after the commissioning and handover phases. Modifications to buildings or plant, provision of technical assistance and the supply of standby personnel are included in this category. The problems and costs of post-commissioning work are reduced by improved project planning and control. It is unusual for vendor engineers to be permanently employed and, even if post-commissioning assistance is engaged for an initial period, a final handover point will be reached and must be provided for. The buyer requires protection of his investment in that facilities must be provided for complete independence in the operation and maintenance functions.

Proving

After buildings or plant are commissioned there may be a preliminary operating period during which the assets are proved under precise operating conditions with the local operatives and maintenance men. In the case of manufacturing plant the supplies and services are proved at this time, also the plant's ability to produce effectively with the standard input materials. Variations in these latter may even cause major redesign.

The effect of the local supplies and services upon plant are important. Typical problems arising are:

1 Unclean oil for hydraulic systems.
2 Unclean or pulsating air for pneumatic systems.
3 An inability to cope with the effluent or waste.
4 'Dirty' electrical supplies (that is, power supplies with peak pulses super-imposed) to electronic equipment.
5 Contaminated or mineralized water.
6 Contaminated atmosphere or fluctuating temperatures.
7 Contamination from nearby plant.
8 Vibration from other sources or from the new plant.
9 Sound effects, reverberation, non-absorbency.

Building Projects

The procedures for appointing architects, surveyors, consulting engineers, designers and contractors for building projects are well established. However, less attention has been paid to the use of buildings maintenance consultants. In most project work the client selects an architect who has quantity surveyors and clerks of works to assist him in the preparation and enforcement of the plan. Contractors are selected for the construction work, also consultants, designers and specialist engineering companies for the services and other installations.

As with plant projects, building projects can benefit substantially from the appointment of a maintenance adviser (see Figure 10:4). His objectives would include:

1   Facilitating disclosure of design technical information by the various contractors.
2   Introduction of maintenance planning and control.
3   Enforcement of product support (technical manuals, specifications, spare parts).
4   Encouraging technical communication between the designers and contractors and the maintenance manager.

This adviser or consultant would liaise with the architects, consulting engineers, designers and contractors and would report back to the project controller.

Safety — New Projects

At the planning stage of a new project a number of aspects of industrial safety require attention. These are:

1   The provision of services (gas, water, etc.) must be planned with safety in mind.
2   Plant layouts must provide for safe working space.
3   Appropriate floor, ventilation and lighting standards must be maintained.
4   Delivery routes for plant must be planned for safety.
5   Adequate and safe arrangements must be made for plant handling.
6   Scaffolding, lifting gear, etc. must meet accepted standards.
7   Suitable arrangements must be made for alarming workers in unsafe conditions.
8   Interpreters must be provided to prevent accidents when plant of foreign manufacture is installed by engineers using a foreign language, if communication becomes difficult.
9   Requirements for safety (interlocks, guards, etc.) must be established and implemented.
10   A definite chain of responsibility to a single project head must be enforced to prevent duplicate or wrong instructions being used.
11   The procurement specification should include this or similar wording: The plant must comply with all statutory requirements.

During installation the following points are important:

1   Lifting and moving must be supervised by a competent person.
2   Instructions for installation and operation must be supplied and verified before use.
3   All supplies should be isolated until connection to the machinery is authorized.
4   Temporary supplies should not be used.
5   Before use, the plant must be examined for
     (*a*)   Adequate safety interlocks.
     (*b*)   Adequate guards.
     (*c*)   Adequate safety procedures.
6   Precautions against fire and against glare must be taken if welding techniques are used.

In the commissioning phase safety features include:

1 The commissioning procedure must be known, understood and followed.
2 All interlocks and guards must be effective.
3 Running machinery should not be started or supplies turned on without due warning.
4 Running machines should be started slowly if speed adjustments are possible.
5 Electrical overloads, safety valves, etc. should be calibrated and checked.
6 All controls and emergency stops should be checked for operability.
7 All operator working positions should be checked for safety, visibility, etc.

Training

On new projects, plans for technical control by the maintenance staff must be made at the planning stage and appropriate training given to the selected personnel. Provision must be made in the procurement specifications for specific plant training but some pre-training is often required. This may include:

1 General craft training.
2 Control systems and instrumentation systems training.
3 Fault-diagnosis and repair-methods training.

This type of training is a precondition of successful operation of new assets, and can form part of a 'maintenance improvement' programme for existing buildings and/or plant.

When the plant to be maintained employs well known principles of operation, the maintenance requirements can be met by the employment of mechanical fitters and electricians, supported by labourers and greasers, with toolmakers being used as necessary to service machine tools. The requirements of the building are met by painters, carpenters, etc. During the design and installation of new plant it is usually possible for key members of the maintenance department to be employed in advance so that they receive some familiarization training on the equipment and machines. This training is supplemented by teams of engineers from the vendor companies who not only install the plant but ensure smooth handover to the maintenance staff. However it is unusual to see a fully documented training programme at this stage and too much training relies upon direct conversation between the two parties. The problem with such training is that it is first generation training only and if there is a labour turnover, or accidents to skilled men with special knowledge, the investor has no safeguard for the large sums of money invested in the new plant or for the return on investment which is expected from the continuance of production.

PROCUREMENT SPECIFICATION

Product support information
The following requirements constitute the contract requirement. (Additional information should be supplied if available.)

1 Six copies of the operating and maintenance manuals and spare-parts lists issued by the equipment subcontractors.

2(a) Operation and maintenance charts
Six copies of operation and maintenance instruction charts with comprehensive descriptive information and diagrams. One set of charts to be framed and glazed for installation at the workplace.

2(b) Operation and maintenance manuals
Six copies of operation and maintenance manuals to British Standard B.S.4884 and the Institution of Plant Engineers' Guide (Reference 4). Drawings are to be photoreduced and incorporated into the manuals to facilitate reference also to reduce volume. All spare parts must be identified clearly by the use of 'exploded' perspective drawings.

Each manual will be printed on paper and bound in hard covers.

Figure 10:1   Extract from plant procurement specification

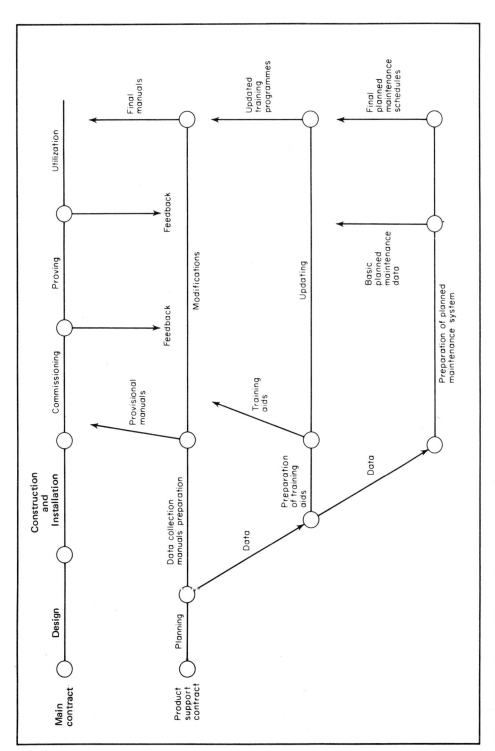

Figure 10:2 Network for product support programme

Factor	Remedy
1. Insufficient attention to reliability and life maintenance predictions during research and development phase.	Improved R and D management disciplines and design analysis.
2. Procurement on lowest tender without regard to possible life maintenance costs.	Increased technical vetting by maintenance manager during procurement.
3. Procurement without specification of and enforcement of product support requirements to be met at time of installation.	Include spares, maintenance manuals, tools, training assistance, commissioning, etc.
4. Insufficient appreciation of role of maintenance by works managers, production managers, etc.	Maintenance appreciation courses for managers of associated departments.
5. Failure to plan the maintenance operation and to budget accordingly.	Information and training for project planners, and chief engineers.
6. Ineffective communication in the maintenance hierarchy.	See items 3 and 8.
7. Inadequate training for maintenance staff beyond basic skills level.	Maintenance training courses of wider scope (fault-finding and repair training, for example).
8. Insufficient management training for engineers required to manage maintenance departments.	Training in communication, management by objectives, budgeting, control and planning, tero-technology and maintenance improvement techniques.

Figure 10:3 **Factors having adverse effect on maintenance efficiency**

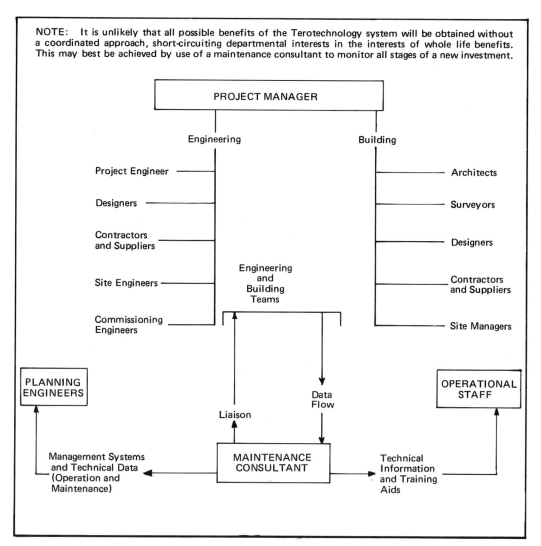

Figure 10:4   Maintenance consultant attached to project team

11

Costing and Budgeting

Costing and budgeting for the maintenance department embraces the provision of financial information on labour and materials expenditure, its allocation to the various cost centres, together with manpower resourcing and the development of objectives with programmes and budgets for meeting them. Cost control must provide for the accurate allocation of costs to departments using the services of the maintenance staff and to construction work and other projects. Feedback from the accounts department includes spending rates in the various sectors and details of conformity with or departure from estimates and budgets.

Cost Codes

The basis for cost control is provided by the use of cost account codes. These facilitate the booking of labour and materials to particular budget headings (capital works, services, etc.), to particular departments (personnel, production, etc.) or to specific machines, factories or plant areas. Typical major code headings might include:

1 Capital projects.
2 Planned preventive maintenance.
3 Workshop services.

Subdivisions of the code provide details of:

1 Office-block lighting maintenance.
2 Chocolate blending line modifications.
3 Bottling line standby labour costs.
4 'G' building maintenance, etc.

Subdivisions are chosen to give the precise information required, to show cost trends in particular sectors, to indicate maintenance budget expenditure not directly attributable to maintenance and to provide guidance for, first, asset replacement policies and, second, future budgeting.

Cost Allocations

The costs attributable to the cost codes consist broadly of wages and salaries, overhead charges, materials costs, transport costs, and sundry items. These costs are summarized by the general accounts department, a typical method being as follows:

1   *Wages*
    (*a*)   Times booked to cost codes extracted from time sheets or clock cards and charged to individual cost codes.
    (*b*)   The balance of time not booked to specific cost codes contributes to the overhead.
    (*c*)   Summaries of the costs to major cost codes (capital projects, etc.) are made to give totals for comparison with budget headings (see later).
    (*d*)   The total expenditure for the period is compared with the budgeted labour figure, and cumulative comparisons·made.

Thus, the system provides labour charges for major and minor cost codes and for budget variance comparisons.

2   *Materials*
    (*a*)   Withdrawals (for normal maintenance) and incoming supplies (for capital projects work) are entered in the stores ledger in the stock control office against specific cost codes.
    (*b*)   Materials charges are extracted in the general accounts office and the cost codes noted.
    (*c*)   Summaries of the materials costs against major and minor cost codes are made to give totals for comparison with budgets.
    (*d*)   The total materials expenditure for the period is compared with the budgeted figure and a cumulative comparison made.

Thus the costs of labour and materials in the areas defined by the cost codes are determined.

Overhead Calculations

The overhead charge made upon maintenance is made up of charges occurring within the maintenance department plus the overhead charges reflected from other departments, for example:

1   Administration.
2   General management.
3   Personnel.

Charges arising within the department include: services, rent and rates, transport and insurance.

Budgets

Figure 11:1 indicates a budget summary form in which the various grades of labour are listed. The numbers of each grade and their annual rate are multiplied to give totals for each labour grade. These figures are then summed to produce a labour total to which is added an agreed percentage for overtime working.

The materials figures indicate those materials directly chargeable to cost codes and those applied indirectly, for example, cleaning materials and small items which do not warrant the cost of individual costing action.

The item 'other costs' refers generally to the overheads section of the budget and includes part of the overall administration costs, the building maintenance costs relevant to the maintenance area, depreciation costs for the maintenance tools and workshop plant, and a percentage of the rents, rates and services costs applicable to that area of the total plant which is occupied by the maintenance department.

The summation of the above items produces a total figure for expenditure in the maintenance department on wages, materials and overheads, to which must be added any special categories such as subcontracted work, special projects and a contingency figure. This contingency should include any expenditure on improvement projects plus an allowance for rises in costs over the period. In the 1970s total maintenance costs have tended to increase at the rate of 8 to 15 per cent per year in line with inflation.

The proportions of the total maintenance expenditure allocated to sections 1 to 4 of the budget vary between industries and according to the accounting techniques used. In some industries the total cost of fuel is the responsibility of the maintenance manager and is included in the maintenance budget. Thus the budget may show:

Maintenance labour	24%
Maintenance materials	39%
Fuel costs	26%
Overheads	11%

Another distortion is introduced by the inclusion of production tool costs in the maintenance budget. Thus, in the example above, the inclusion of new rolls for the rolling machines has inflated the materials costs to 39 per cent.

Objectives and Strategies

When producing a departmental business plan it is necessary in the written part of the budget to define objectives and strategies for the department in the coming year. Objectives to be set for the maintenance department will include the implementation of planned maintenance programmes, the completion of certain capital works and the operation of a planned overhaul programme. A forward projection of the current situation, when compared with the above, will indicate any performance gaps which have to be bridged by selected strategies. These may include the use of subcontract labour, subcontracting projects and the delay of non-urgent work. This becomes the management plan for the department. One objective for the department might be the reduction of resources allocated to corrective and emergency maintenance and an increase in planned preventive work.

Cost Reports

The maintenance manager will require from the accounts department management information relating to:

1   Comparison of actual spending with business plan.
2   Detailed analyses of important variances.
3   Maintenance cost reports.
4   Capital project costs (if these are managed by the maintenance department).

The comparison of actual spending with the business plan begins with summaries under the headings shown on the plan and may be extended to any depth required for analysis (Figure 11:2). Computer print-outs provide a convenient means for extensive analyses of costs. Sources of management information are illustrated by Figure 11:3.

Life Cycle Costing

The life cycle costs of an asset include the initial costs (the total costs of procurement and setting to work), the costs of ownership during the life cycle, and the costs of downtime. When initial costs are calculated it is important to include the costs of services, commissioning, product support and ancillary equipment as described in Chapter 10 'Procurement'. The costs of ownership include the annual costs of operation and maintenance, multiplied and factored for the life term, together with the costs or income expected when the asset is disposed of. The costs from downtime include loss of use, repair costs and consequential damage, and will provide evidence for replacement decisions.

The introduction of current cost accounting (CCA) revalues assets on a replacement cost basis. Each item on the asset register is valued not on standard depreciation but on the real cost of replacing the asset in the current fiscal year. This shows the present worth to the investor when inflation is considered. The valuation of assets in these terms requires frequent assessment of life cycle costs to date, together with predictions of future costs and life cycle expectations. Maintenance costs can be usefully expressed in terms of the replacement value, instead of initial costs only.

$$\frac{\text{Annual maintenance cost}}{\text{Current replacement cost}} \times \frac{100}{1} \%$$

Inflation affects both of these quantities and a meaningful expression of the maintenance costs is obtained.

Manpower Resourcing

The basic labour allocations have to be made in accordance with the objectives for the year, using the previous year as a starting point. Figure 11:4 gives some indication of the items for which labour will be allocated. As stated earlier there must be a prime objective of moving resources from item 3 to item 1, and this has been successfully accomplished in many plants. What usually happens is that a slight tendency to over-maintain appears at first but as the corrective maintenance and downtime figures reduce, there comes an opportunity to rationalize the preventive maintenance schedules in accordance with the known requirements of the plant items. The frequency of maintenance activities is lengthened as history records indicate the exact requirement of the plant, thus releasing labour for other duties (for example, capital project work or local spares manufacture).

Item 2 on the list of labour allocations is planned standby maintenance. This refers to plant situations where the production loss at breakdown is so high that having a maintenance man on permanent standby is an economic proposition. It is usual to exclude such plant from the general planned maintenance work programme, the work specifications and frequencies being given to the standby personnel. Feedback and records are of course still essential. Item 4, capital projects, requires a full knowledge of the construction procurement plans but if these are known far enough in advance estimates can be obtained for all work from reliable subcontractors and this simplifies any division of the work between internal and contract labour.

Item 5, 'Workshop time', refers to such tasks as local manufacture of spares, maintenance and grading of spares, test gear construction, planned overhauls, maintenance improvement projects, etc. Failure to identify these items inhibits adequate budgeting in subsequent years and, providing that useful records are kept for analysis purposes, these costs benefit from a thorough consideration.

Item 6 is of real importance. The forgotten maintenance department is soon in the public eye if the plant is unfit to restart after a closed period. In large plants planning for annual shutdown is a continuous process with a special department, large planning boards and even computers. In many smaller companies the shutdown is often merely an occasion for overtime working. The need for planning and for labour allocation, particularly where subcontract staff are used, is obvious.

Figure 11:5 indicates the next stage of resource planning in which a shortfall or a surplus of man-hours is identified and suitable strategies adopted. A surplus would indicate that further capital work can be undertaken. A shortfall indicates that more capital work can be subcontracted or that extra staff are required. In the latter case there may be requirements for consultancy or other expert services to review operations. Additional information will have to be provided in the business plan if, for example, the planned overhaul is to be concentrated in the annual two-week closure period. Then there will be an obvious requirement for subcontract assistance, a requirement which will need some justification.

The budgeting and cost control aspects of maintenance management are frequently described by managers as a chore; this is particularly noticeable in situations where the maintenance manager has been 'given' the extra work instead of being trained into it, and where the maintenance manager has difficulty in getting contributory information from his assistants because they too lack formal training in business management techniques. This indicates that formal cost control systems require introduction and familiarization training as do any other new techniques. The adoption of formal budgets can be a limiting factor in the beginning, much to the annoyance of managers trying to meet changing programmes, but, when the techniques are fully understood, budgets can be used to advantage in many situations. The written part of the budget, defining the objectives and strategies, is very important and the retention of some flexibility (for example, in transferring money from one expenditure heading to another) provides for changes in these strategies to meet changes in balance between the various sections of the total budget figure. Once fully understood, formal budgeting is a useful discipline not only in predicting and controlling expenditure but in encouraging the prediction and preplanning of activity with the necessary resourcing to meet the plan.

MAINTENANCE BUDGET		NO.	RATE	£
(1) Salaries (inclusive)	Foremen	– – –	– – – –	
	Fitters	– – –	– – – –	
	Electricians	– – –	– – – –	
	Instrument	– – –	– – – –	
	Greasers	– – –	– – –	
	Others	– – –	– – –	
	Total			– – – – –
	Overtime 15%			– – – – –
(2) Materials	Direct		– – – –	
	Indirect		– – –	
	Total			– – – –
(3) Other costs	Administration		– – – –	
	Proportion of building maintenance		– – –	
	Depreciation		– – –	
	Proportion of rent and rates		– – –	
	Proportion of heating and services		– – –	
	Insurances		– –	
	Other costs		– –	
	Total			– – – –
(4) Subcontract labour			– – –	
Subcontract projects			– – –	
Maintenance improvement and contingency			– – –	
	Total			– – – –
	Grand total			– – – – – –

Figure 11:1   Typical budget summary sheet

Budget variance report							
Date				Dept.			
Monthly costs				Cumulative costs			
Code	Budget	Actual	Variance	Budget	Actual	Variance	

Maintenance costs report				
Month		Dept.		
Code	Labour	Materials	Total	Cumulative

Capital project report				
Code		Month		Project
Sub-code	Labour	Materials	Total	Cumulative

Figure 11:2   Typical cost report forms

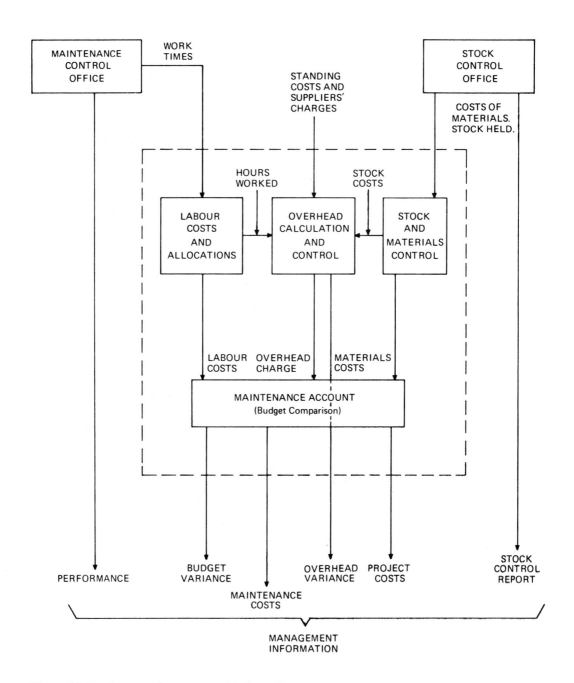

Figure 11:3   Sources of management information

Maintenance labour allocations	Grades of labour				
	Inst.	Elect.	Mech.	Lub.	Other
1 Planned preventive maintenance					
2 Planned standby maintenance					
3 Corrective and emergency work					
4 Capital projects					
5 Workshop time					
6 Planned overhaul					
Totals					

Figure 11:4   Labour allocation chart

Resource plan		Grades of labour				
		Inst.	Elect.	Mech.	Lub.	Other
Planned labour allocation						
Available labour force						
Shortfall/surplus						
Action plan	Subcontract labour					
	Subcontract project					
	Recruitment					
	Total hours					

Figure 11:5   Resource planning table

Appendix 1

Extract from Procurement Checklist
(Maintenance and Product Support Items)

1 *Maintainability*

(a) Will reliability and maintainability studies and MTTR/MTBF predictions be provided?

Notes

Dates required for provisional and revised failure and repair predictions.

(b) Will D.O.M. (design-out-maintenance) be practised?

Includes anti-corrosion methods.

(c) Will dependency structure of design be analysed?

Dependency charts indicate component redundancies and undue dependencies.

(d) Does design include coordinated test and repair strategy?

Physical access/test gear/spares holdings/technical information to be integrated.

(e) Is condition monitoring or surveillance to be provided for?

Data link to centralized surveillance, built-in analysis instrumentation or attachments for portable monitors.

(f) Life cycle costing. Has a cost study been completed and comparisons made with other existing designs (if any) or other possible designs? (If user is to make this study has adequate data been provided?)

Cost factors include:
Interest on total capital cost.
Cost of maintenance budget.
Cost of interest on spares.
Depreciation charges.
Cost of space and services.
Cost of downtime predicted or planned.
Cost of relocation or disposal.

(*g*) Have standardization prospects
       (if any) been studied?

Is compatibility of installation or
components with previous types
possible?

(*h*) What level of supplier maintenance
       is required?

Supplier maintenance may be
costly and reduce in-plant skills
levels.

(*i*) Will supplier provide liaison facilities
       for user's maintenance team and/or
       consultants?

2   *Maintenance System*
   (*a*) Will maintenance information be
          provided as part of the test/repair
          policy?
   (*b*) Will user's asset register information
          be provided?
   (*c*) Will maintenance schedules, with
          frequencies, be provided for
          evaluation?
   (*d*) Is fast fault-diagnosis provided for?
   (*e*) Will rationalized lubrication schedules
          be provided?
   (*f*) Will recommended spares lists be
          available for review by user?

Deviations from user's standards
to be agreed.
Compatibility with existing
stocks to be reviewed.
Standardization to be studied.

   (*g*) What are the maintenance manning
          requirements?
   (*h*) Special tools, handling equipment
          and test gear. Have these require-
          ments been listed and costed?
   (*i*) Will drawings be provided for local
          manufacture of spare parts?

Review skills requirements.
Consolidate manning programme

3   *Quality and Reliability*
   (*a*) Has supplier applied quality control
          throughout?
   (*b*) Does supplier operate a quality
          management system?
   (*c*) Has supplier a quality rating?
   (*d*) Will quality assurance specifications
          (shop-test specifications and results)
          be provided?

Materials, components and
assemblies to be covered.
Responsibility to a manager or
director is essential.

Notes

(*e*) Will a safety report be made?

Safety aspects require a study before acceptance of the proposed design.

4   *Delivery and Installation*

(*a*) Will a delivery/installation management plan be submitted?

Dates required.

(*b*) Does supplier's insurance provision cover all parties at this time?

Third party plant and personnel to be covered.

(*c*) Are services/foundations specified and costed?

(*d*) Are statutory requirements for effluent, etc. provided for?

(*e*) Has production area (if not new) been reviewed for new requirements?

Lighting, access, floor loading, etc.

(*f*) Will installation drawings be available for review?

Date required.

(*g*) Is supplier to undertake delivery and installation?

Define responsibilities for supply/hire of handling equipment, etc.

5   *Commissioning*

(*a*) Will plant be commissioned by vendor or by commissioning consultants?

Consultants are often preferred.

(*b*) Will supplier provide liaison facilities for the commissioning consultants?

(*c*) Is adequate insurance cover arranged for commissioning period?

By supplier or by consultant firm.

(*d*) Is commissioning plan to be presented?

Date required.

(*e*) Will safety officer be appointed or consulted?

(*f*) What system of recording commissioning period modifications will be adopted?

This recording is vital.

(*g*) What arrangements will be made for supply of materials and disposal of effluent or product waste during commissioning?

6   *Training*   *Notes*
     (*a*)   What arrangements will be made for   Training programmes must be
             maintenance staff training in the   documented and are required
             manufacturing period, delivery/   in provisional form prior to
             installation and commissioning   installation so that courses may
             periods?   be planned.

7   *Product Support*
     (*a*)   Will operating and maintenance
             information be provided by all
             suppliers in respect of all items
             procured?
     (*b*)   Will the total information on a   Supplier submissions must be
             multi-supplier project be coordinated   indexed to form a technical
             and by whom?   library and must be
              (i) Management of prime supplier, or   standardized.
              (ii) Consultant.
     (*c*)   Will preliminary information (drawings   Date required.
             and draft manuals) be available for
             training course planning?
     (*d*)   Will technical manuals conform to   Specification TM/9/74 is avail-
             TM/9/74 or BS 4884 standards?   able from the Institution of Plant
                                                       Engineers, London.
     (*e*)   Are illustrated spares lists provided?   These lists may be incorporated
             Are the component manufacturers'   in the manuals.
             names and reference numbers quoted?
     (*f*)   Are operating procedures provided
             separately or in the technical manuals?
     (*g*)   Will manufacturing and design drawings   Number of prints to be specified
             be supplied?   plus microfilm masters.
     (*h*)   Will product support manuals be
             prepared by:
              (i) In-plant engineers
              (ii) Publishing contractors for supplier
              (iii) Consultants/contractors for user?
     (*i*)   Will maintenance schedules be   These may be included in the
             provided?   technical manuals.
     (*j*)   Will amendment lists be issued as   This applies to manuals, spares
             standard updating procedure?   lists and training programmes.
     (*k*)   When will final technical manuals,   State dates and quantities.
             training programmes and spares lists
             be issued?

8   *Costing*   *Notes*
    (*a*) Will the following cost details of each   These costs permit unit price to
           unit price be provided: be isolated and the support costs
           (i) Cost of recommended spares   evaluated against use of specialist
           (ii) Cost of training assistance   contractors, consultants, training
           (iii) Cost of product support   schools, etc.
           (iv) Cost of commissioning by
                   vendor engineers
           (v) Other vendor assistance costs.

9   *Penalties*
    (*a*) Will vendor accept full penalties on
           these maintenance support aspects
           as on the installation itself?

Appendix 2

Specification for Contents of Maintenance Manual

NOTE: A complete specification (TM/9/74) is published by the Institution of Plant Engineers (Reference 4).

Section 1. This section describes the purpose of the machine and outlines its supply requirements and performance characteristics. A list of all relevant data is given and warnings of any hazards in connection with the use of this particular type of plant.

Where appropriate the information in section 1 may be abbreviated and a comprehensive specification issued as a separate document. This document would be referenced to section 1.

Section 2. This section must provide complete operator information to the level required and must be suitable for production as a separate document or as instruction cards if required for operator usage.

The section begins with a description of the various operating modes. These may vary with the method of control (manual, auto, remote, etc.), with the input material (paper, plastic, etc.) or with the end product requirement (plain boxes, printed boxes, die-cut boxes, etc.).

Operating instructions for each mode follow and these must be complete in each case, without cross-reference to other modes. Emergency procedures are required, also safety notes. Any safety note referring to a particular action must precede the instruction for that action. For example:

5 Open delivery chute selector.
  Safety note: Ensure all personnel are clear of machine.
6 Press START button.

Operator fault-diagnostic procedures must be included, preferably in flow chart form. (These reduce unnecessary requests for maintenance services.) Any maintenance or adjustments to be performed by the operator must be specified in detail. Finally the procedure for monitoring and reporting failures must be described so that maximum assistance is given to repair men.

Section 3. The technical description must be presented in logical order commencing with system or overall machine details, then description of individual equipment items, or subassemblies and finally ancillary items, test gear, etc. The volume of text must be kept to a minimum and illustrations used wherever possible. Illustrations must be annotated with useful information and part identifications. (Unannotated photographs are of little use in maintenance.) All part names used in the technical description should correspond to those used in the parts list.

Section 4. The section must begin with full instructions for handling, transportation and unpacking. Special lifting gear, access problems, plant security and personnel safety notes are necessary. The section must then provide full illustrated procedures for installation, assembly, connection of supplies and preparation for commissioning.

Commissioning and proving procedures are required. These will include details of materials and services needed during this period. If the plant is to be commissioned to a quality assurance specification provided by a consultant or by the vendor this will be a separate document referred to in this section.

Finally the section must provide full instructions for relocation of the plant (if this is possible using domestic personnel) in the event of plant layout changes, also precautions to be taken in the event of it being placed in storage. Disposal instructions are important and will include proposals for re-use or re-sale, details of dismantling and recovery of materials from the plant, its foundations and ancillaries, also details of any procedures necessary to ensure safety of personnel or to protect the environment. (For example, disposal instructions for lead, acid or other plants.)

Section 5. Full instructions are required for maintenance, beginning with fault diagnosis routines which are best presented in chart form. These should be suitable for extraction from the manual for use as charts in the workshop.

Corrective maintenance instructions are required in two parts – minor and major. Minor maintenance tasks include calibration and adjustment procedures and minor repair instructions. Major maintenance work includes removal-to-workshop procedures (if necessary), removal and replacement instructions for replaceable units, repair and overhaul procedures (dismantling, repair or overhaul, and reassembly) and scheduled repair instructions. All maintenance instructions should include procedures for return to service and testing.

Section 6. Maintenance schedules are required for preventive work (monitoring, inspection, lubrication, cleaning, testing, replenishment) giving precise details and recommended frequencies. These must be complete without reference to other parts of the manual and must be suitable for use as individual work cards if necessary.

Calibration schedules must be included here if not included in section 2. These must provide complete information for machine audits. Other scheduled work (for example, scheduled repair and replacement) must be included in this section. If these operations require extensive description or illustration cross references to the appropriate parts of section 5 are made. This reduces the volume of information necessary in this section. Complex work of a scheduled nature (for example an annual overhaul with replacement of major parts) requires work schedules, estimated times and network plans.

General notes (Sections 5 and 6)

All corrective maintenance instructions must be adequately illustrated and provide step-by-step sequences suitable for use as work specifications. Details of special tools, test gear, test rigs and handling equipment are required. Fits and clearances diagrams are required. Safety procedures and notes for both personnel and for plant or components are to be included.

Preventive maintenance instructions must be complete and illustrated to facilitate recognition of parts, test points, lubrication points, etc. Instructions should be presented as tables, flow charts or check lists suitable for the development of routes and work times in a planned preventive maintenance system.

Section 7. The parts lists must be preceded by identification drawings for the plant layout, for the system or for the machine. These identify the major equipment items in a system or the major assemblies on a machine, and define their position in the parts list. The items or assemblies are then dealt with in turn, 'exploded' drawings, parts lists, part numbers, part names and recommended spares stocks being provided for each. If the list of recommended spares varies widely for various plant applications the vendor may be permitted to list these separately to reduce production costs for the manual. Part names as used in these lists must conform to those used elsewhere in the manual, although reversals are permitted, for example:

> MANUAL   — Boxwheel coupler gear.
> PARTS LIST — Gear, boxwheel coupler.

Section 8. Modifications made to the plant prior to acceptance, including those made during commissioning or as post-design work by vendor engineers must be recorded to the same standard as used in the manual. Bulletins, amendments or replacement pages must be issued to all sections affected, including operating procedures. Illustrations, lists of parts, technical descriptions and maintenance instructions are required. The manual should be issued in loose-leaf form so as to simplify the incorporation of modifications.

Modification instructions for the users must be to the standard used for the manual and must include: detailed procedures, details of new or replaced parts, disposal instructions for redundant parts, detailed operating and maintenance instructions, parts lists, changes to parts stocks, and revised or additional technical manual pages.

A Guide to Presentation

Mention has been made of the various ways of presenting technical information for maintenance. In some plant situations the enforcement of lengthy specifications for technical manual requirements has produced thick volumes which are rarely used because they are so unsuitable for the workshop floor. In a similar way, insistence on full technical descriptions can result in volumes of text which is not only time-consuming and expensive to read but tends to obscure the technical detail. For example, a tolerance figure may be difficult to locate if presented within a long paragraph of text. Worse still, it may be omitted and the engineer committed to reading a whole paragraph for nothing.

Thus, all information must be presented for rapid access and as comprehensively as possible. The technical manual should be produced as a number of volumes if necessary. These may be divided in various ways:

Example 1	Volume 1	Operator's Manual
	Volume 2	Scheduled Maintenance
	Etc.	
Example 2	Volume 1	Mixer Plant
	Volume 2	Drying Plant
		. . . etc.

The various sections in each manual should be separated by coloured cards to facilitate reference.

Some sections of the manual may be produced separately as plasticized cards. This technique is useful for operator's instructions, preventive maintenance instructions and fault-finding charts. Plant layout drawings and other items from the manual should be reproduced as wall charts if the information is more accessible in that form. In some plants, pages from the manual are repeated on microfilm. These may be used in the factory on portable viewing devices or may be projected for discussion and reference purposes. The technical manual is the standard form of information disclosure used by equipment vendors but an open mind on presentation methods can result in reduced information retrieval times.

One important aspect of presentation already referred to is the use of illustrations rather than words. Some of the methods used are:

1   Flow charts (algorithms) – the presentation of operating instructions and fault-finding routines in algorithm form reduces learning times and encourages local thinking by those using the charts.

2   Dependency charts – these charts show the inter-dependency of the various

parts of the plant so that fault-finding times can be reduced.

3   Descriptive illustrations — in section 3 of the manual it is good practice to use illustrations with the description added, to replace pages of descriptive text. This makes information easier and quicker to retrieve.

4   'Exploded' drawings — these are frequently used in parts lists but can be used again in section 5 of the manual to describe the procedures for dismantling, repair and assembly. The necessary text can be positioned on or around the drawing and referenced to it.

5   Illustrated maintenance procedures — in sections 5 and 6 of the manual illustrations can be used as the basis for presenting the maintenance procedures. These also reduce access time and are convenient for removal from the manual for use as work cards.

6   Lubrication drawings — these also consist of drawings of the plant with instructions and symbols attached to show the type of lubricant and method of application.

7   Illustrated spares lists — spares lists are not acceptable unless linked to 'exploded' drawings.

The paper used in technical manuals should be medium-weight and able to resist tearing from the binder used. Special oil-resistant or plastic-coated papers are not necessary. If manuals are to be used for bench work it is better to remove appropriate pages and to use them in plastic containers or as wall charts with suitable protection. All circuit and other diagrams should be produced on one side of the paper only so that they may be converted to wall charts if necessary without losing information from the other side. The old practice of printing all diagrams on long sheets of paper so that they stand clear of the text is to be deplored. This makes the manual bulky, the long folded sheets tear and if the illustrations are positioned correctly in the manual and the volume of text pages reduced there are no problems of location and reference to make this practice necessary.

All drawings must be reduced to an appropriate size and bound within the manual. Each manual and each section or chapter must have contents pages which facilitate reference to specific items of text and illustration.

All manuals must be loose-leaf and contained in multi-ring binders to reduce the risk of page losses. The binding mechanisms must be of the ring type (preferably D-ring) so that opened manuals will lie flat.

Printing must be by letterpress or offset litho. Photocopied, duplicated and dyeline copies are not acceptable.

The title of each manual must appear upon the front and the spine of the binder.

Appendix 3

References

1 *Report by the Working Party on Maintenance Engineering*, Her Majesty's Stationery Office.
2 *The Terotechnology Handbook*, Her Majesty's Stationery Office.
3 *Plant Information Exchange*, National Terotechnology Centre, Cleeve Road, Leatherhead, Surrey.
4 *Technical Manuals – A Guide to Users' Requirements*, Institution of Plant Engineers, 138 Buckingham Palace Road, London, SW1.
5 *International Language for Servicing and Maintenance*, M and E White Consultants Ltd., P.O. Box 257, West Byfleet, Surrey.
6 *Logistics*, M and E White Consultants Ltd., P.O. Box 257, West Byfleet, Surrey.

Index